HOLD THEM NEAR

HOLD THEM NEAR

Catherine Beachy Yoder

Catherine Yoder 2/26/91

STEP AHEAD, LTD.
PUBLISHING DIVISION
New Paris, Indiana

All Scripture quotations from the King James Version

Cover photo by Marvin Beachy

Step Ahead, Ltd.
Publishing Division
18638 County Road 46
New Paris, Indiana 46553

First Printing   July, 1990
Second Printing   October, 1990
Third Printing   January, 1991

Printed in the United States of America

*This book is dedicated to my mother, Amy,
for her tireless encouragement,
and to all the Beachys and Hochstetlers
who have been so helpful and supportive!*

Hold tight to the sound of the music of living,
Happy songs from the laughter of children at play;
Hold my hand as we run
Through the sweet fragrant meadows,
Making memories of what was today.

Tiny voice that I hear is my little girl calling
For daddy to hear just what she has to say;
And my little son
Running there by the hillside
May never be quite like today.

Tender words, gentle touch and a good cup of coffee,
And someone who loves me and wants me to stay;
***HOLD THEM NEAR** while they're here*
And don't wait for tomorrow
To look back and wish for today.

We have this moment to hold in our hands
And to touch as it slips through our fingers like sand.
Yesterday's gone and tomorrow may never come,
But we have this moment today.

Introduction

"To everything there is a season, and a time to every purpose under the heaven; A time to be born, and a time to die...A time to weep and a time to laugh...a time to keep..."

Ecclesiastes 3:1-6

For the family that once lived in the house on the cover, this book has provided a time to remember. It is a time to remember the joys and sorrows of those days long past that molded their lives. It is a time to remember the importance of cherishing each moment of life, and holding loved ones near while one has that privilege.

The story you are about to read really happened. Many details have become blurred with time, but I have reconstructed them the best I could, in the hope that you will see how God can, and does, work through heartaches to bring joy into the lives of ordinary people. It is the desire of my grandparents, Noah and Lizzie Ann (Kurtz) Beachy, as it would have been of my paternal grandmother, the late Sara (Hochstetler) Beachy, that God is glorified in this story. If God becomes more real to you through this book, if you can trust Him more fully in your daily life, our prayers are answered.

-Catherine (Beachy) Yoder

Chapter One

The baby slept.

Mary Lou wearily pushed back a strand of dark hair. She rose cautiously from the rocker and laid Henry on the couch. "Judy, he's finally sleeping," Mary Lou whispered to her three-year-old sister.

"Let's go tell Mommy!" Judy's blue eyes sparkled with energy and excitement.

"Mommy will be so glad! She said he didn't sleep much last night."

Hand-in-hand the girls hurried through the darkened house to their coats. They dressed quickly for the January cold and ran across the snowy lawn to the washline.

Sara Beachy smiled as she saw the girls coming. Her "little helpers," she called them. With five children under seven there certainly was a lot of work to be done! Her dark coat blew around her slight form, and her fingers stung from the cold as she pinned up another diaper.

"They must have put Henry to sleep," she mused. "He's been crying so much all weekend! I wonder what's wrong with him! The doctor thought it was indigestion, but his suggestion to give soda water hasn't helped much. I hope keeping the house dark fools him into sleeping all morning."

"Mommy, he's sleeping!" Judy announced.

"Good for you, girls! I'm just done here, so I'll come in and check on him. Mary Lou, why don't you carry the basket for me?"

The trio walked toward the old farmhouse. Peaceful countryside sparkled in the winter sun. Sara relaxed a bit, feeling the weariness in her bones. "God, give me the strength for this Monday," she prayed.

They walked up the steps and entered the sudden dimness of the house. As the three crossed the room to the couch, Sara intuitively stiffened. "Something's wrong here," she said, almost to herself. Just then the baby threw his tiny arms into the air and drew in a raspy breath. Instinctively Sara knew it was his last.

Judy's wide-eyed gaze traveled from the still form on the couch to her mother's frozen face. "Mommy, Mommy, what's wrong?"

"He's dead." Sara's clipped words broke the news to the children. She picked up the body of her darling baby and cradled him to herself.

Thoughts spun through her tired brain:
"...must tell Noah...be brave for the
girls...Henry's gone...turn off the washing
machine...check on Barbara Jean...my baby
is dead...could I have done something better
for him?..." Tears trickled down her cheeks.

Mary Lou and Judy stood transfixed next to
the quiet couch. Sara raised her weary gaze to
see four searching eyes fixed on her face. She
could imagine the girls were wondering if it was
their fault that Henry had died. They probably
thought only animals and old people died. She
could read fear and bewilderment in their faces.
Sara's calm demeanor snapped back into place.
These children needed her; personal grief would
have to wait. Gently she laid down the lifeless
form and turned to hug the girls. "Let's go check
on Barbara Jean and then find Dad and Marvin,"
she told them.

They walked over to Barbara Jean's bed.
Even in sleep the twenty-one month old was
adorable. Her golden curls were scattered over
the pillow, and a faint flush gave her cheeks a
rosy glow. "Such a perfect child," Sara thought
indulgently. Then she was jerked back to reality. Barbara Jean was fine. Now she needed
Noah.

All bundled up, the three tramped to the
barn. Inside, the familiar odor of horses and hay,

cows and feed surrounded them with pungent warmth. Tall, broad-shouldered Noah and six-year-old Marvin were working together. At the sound of the door they turned, impatient at the interruption. One look at Sara's pale face told Noah there was bad news. "What's wrong?" he asked brusquely.

Sara looked past the fierce black beard into the caring blue eyes. Bluntness was best, she decided. "Henry just died." Flatly, without emotion—she had to keep a hold on herself.

"What?" Marvin's pitchfork stood still beside his father's.

"What happened?" Noah urged his wife.

"I asked the girls to take turns rocking him while I hung out the laundry. After awhile they came and told me he was sleeping. I went in to check on everything, and he just threw his hands in the air and he was gone!"

"Oh, no," Noah breathed. Without another word the family filed out of the warm barn and into the house. The sight of the still body broke their reserves, and the tears began to come. Clinging together, parents and children grieved. Henry was such a precious part of the family! Noah grieved for his second son. Mary Lou and Judy were faced with the grim reality of death. Their cuddly little brother wouldn't be here anymore.

Marvin looked around wide-eyed. He knew Henry had been sick, but he had no idea death was so close. And he had been looking forward so much to having another boy to help him with the work! His sturdy young frame shook with sobs. Sara squeezed his hand through her own pain. "God, I don't understand why this happened! I do thank You for our other children, though. Help us help them through this sorrow."

Noah finally looked at his wife. "What do we do first?"

"We need to make lots of phone calls, I guess. First the Ferguson Funeral Home, of course; then call your folks, and get a message to my folks...."

"Mama, Mama!" Barbara Jean's little feet pattered across the floor. Her just-awakened smile always thrilled Sara in a special way. She reached out to pick her up. "You cry?" Barbara Jean's finger patted Sara's still-damp cheek.

"Honey, Henry just died, so Mommy's sad." Of course the child couldn't understand, but in her own charming way she could soothe a bit of the hurt. Sara hugged her tightly.

Still in a daze, Noah began to make calls and break the news. He was glad the Amish church allowed telephones in rental houses. He wasn't ready to face anyone just yet.

Noah's parents, Eli C. and Mary Ann Beachy,

weren't home, but his younger brother was. "Neil, could you give the folks a message right away? You know Henry's been sick all weekend? Well, he just died. . . . Thanks for taking the message."

As Noah rang the operator to call Nappanee, Indiana, Sara thought back to the month before. They had had such a happy time with her family out there at Christmas. Her sisters who lived there, Susie, Barbara, and Wilma, had enjoyed fussing over all the children, especially pink-cheeked Barbara Jean. The little girl was so shy she had clung to Noah most of the time though, since Sara was busy with two-month-old Henry. . . .

The call went through. "Hello? Hello, this is Noah Beachy from Plain City, Ohio calling. Could you get a message to your neighbors, Henry and Mary Hochstetler, right away? Our baby, Henry, just died. . . . "

In an amazingly short time Eli C's drove up the long lane. Although they had been in the midst of butchering at Alvin Kramer's, this was much more important. They had immediately dropped everything to come where they were needed.

Just behind them came Mr. Ferguson, the undertaker. He had buried many Amish babies, but this was a miserable time of year to have a funeral.

Noah helped Mr. Ferguson with the body, then drew Sara aside. "I should go to Abe Miller's and order a casket. Do you think we'd want the funeral on Wednesday? I'll stop by your sister Christena's and also let the bishop know. You'll be all right since Mom's here, won't you?"

Silently Sara nodded. She was already drawing on inner resources she wasn't fully aware she had. "I'll be okay," she reassured him in an almost-steady voice.

Eli C. allowed his son the needed time for introspection as they drove down the road. Finally Noah expressed his thoughts. "I know we don't have much money, but I should have called the doctor out to the house. How could he tell over the phone that the baby just had a stomachache? Maybe Henry's death is my fault."

"You're doing the very best you know how in raising your family," Eli comforted. "Now you just have to commit this situation to God and trust Him."

Soon the errands were completed, and Noah and Eli turned back up the long drive at home. Already a row of buggies lined the fences. News spread rapidly in this small Ohio community!

Inside the house Noah found a quiet bustle of activity. Delicious aromas already drifted from the kitchen, and someone at the treadle sewing machine was running up a simple white burial gown. A thoughtful neighbor had gathered the children and was reading them a story to keep them quiet. It was a bustle that would continue until after the funeral.

The days were a blur to the young family. In keeping with Amish tradition, they would bring the body to the house, dress it themselves, and have the viewing there. People filled the house at all hours. Food was served; the house was cleaned. Tears were shed and dried. The Indiana relatives arrived Tuesday evening and shared the grief.

One thing stood out to the children more than all the rest—the smell. For years they would remember the sickly-sweet smell that accompanied the cotton-wrapped body of their brother when the undertaker returned it. The odor permeated the house and cast a pall of bleakness over everything. Their every breath reminded them their lives would never be quite the same again.

The funeral was held Wednesday at neighbor Roy Miller's, since their house was larger than Noah's. In spite of the cold weather, the home was filled with the young couple's friends. Everyone appreciated Sara's helpfulness and Noah's friendliness. Now it was their turn to give support.

It was only a short trip from the Miller house

to the cemetery after the service. Marvin, Mary Lou, and Judy huddled close to their parents in the corner of the snowy graveyard. Brown dirt seemed so out of place in the pristine whiteness! The children listened solemnly to the black-clad bishop as his voice led out in the familiar German:

> *Gute Nacht, ihr meine Lieben;*
> *Gute Nacht, ihr herzensfreund;*
> *Gute Nacht, die sich betruben,*
> *Und aus Lieb fur mich jetzh weint...*

Many voices joined in song, repeating the lines from the ten-verse poem as men began to cover the simple casket with earth. Sara heard the long benediction through a fog of grief. Someday, she knew, those words would comfort her, but not yet.

> *Good Night, to my beloved;*
> *Good Night, my heartfelt friends;*
> *Good Night to those that sorrow,*
> *And because of love for me you weep,*
> *Even though I depart from you,*
> *And you lay my body in the grave,*
> *It will rise again,*
> *And I will see you eternally.*
>
> *Because my troubles now have ended,*
> *For this my beloved parents are glad,*

Hold Them Near

Thank God for working out His love,
And be no more burdened with sorrow for me.
Father, Mother, so good night,
Remember what God does is done well;
Even though your hearts do sorrow,
He loves me and you as well. [†]

Sara couldn't feel that love right now. She hoped with all her aching heart that soon she would.

[†] Translated by Daniel Bontrager from *Liedersammlung* (Amish German Hymnal).

hursday was empty.

Disconsolately the children wandered through the house. Barbara Jean often wiped her runny nose on Sara's worn apron. The older girls tried to keep her amused in spite of their own listlessness. Marvin escaped the gloomy atmosphere by spending time outside with his dad. Sara mourned silently as she went on with her work. Her hands seemed so empty, and her ears were still tuned to catch that baby-cry she was so familiar with.

"It must have been the Lord's will," she reasoned. "Even though I don't understand it, He will give me the strength to go on."

So, she went on. She comforted Noah, answered Marvin's questions, kept the girls neatly braided. When Sunday came, they all bundled up and attended church services as usual.

The orderly service brought a measure of peace to Sara's troubled heart. The plainly-dressed women with their crisp white coverings and aprons, and openly-sympathetic faces were so dear to her! Across the room she watched Noah find a spot on the backless bench next to Melvin Miller, who was visiting from a neighboring district today. Noah's face had grown some new wrinkles this week. She was thankful he had good friends like Melvin to fellowship with. Inadvertently she smiled a bit as she remembered the fence-jumping goat those two had shot last fall. How they had laughed over the stubborn billy goat who took ten shots directly to his head before his legs buckled under him! But this morning both men were totally sober-minded.

"O, Gott, Vader, wir loben dich. . . . " (O, God, Father, we praise You. . . .) Voices in unison carried the familiar tune of the *Lobe* song, which was the second hymn sung each service. Sara began to relax the tense hold she had kept on herself all week. Hungry for refreshment, she drank in the words of the minister. *"I am the resurrection and the life: He that believeth in Me, though he were dead, yet shall he live." John 11:25.*

Sara shifted the weight of sleeping Barbara Jean from one arm to the other. "Just think of the life Henry is experiencing right now, safe and healthy forever in Heaven," she marvelled. The grief would take time to heal, but a bit of the sharp sting was already being relieved.

After church many friends surrounded the family again with condolences. "At least you still have Barbara Jean," one of the women said.

"She is just so pretty!" another remarked.

"Yes, I know. I always feel like I'm holding an angel with her," Sara confessed shamefacedly. "It will be hard to teach her humility, I'm afraid." Sara could not admit even to these friends her deep feelings about this obviously special child. In fact, Sara was almost afraid to even take Barbara Jean to town for fear the golden-haired charmer would be kidnapped. Last summer one time Barbara Jean's bonnet had blown off, and an "English" (non-Amish) man ran to catch it. When he returned, he just exclaimed over and over about how beautiful the child was. Besides, no other child of Sara's had ever toilet-trained themselves, or wiped their own nose, or didn't make a mess while eating, or never needed a spanking!

"Remember the morning she was born?" Sara's sister Christena had joined the conversation, glad to hear Sara talking about something other than Henry's death. "It was a frosty April morning, and each twig and blade of grass was just sparkling white. I came over while Noah went for the doctor. By the time the doctor arrived, the excitement was all over. Barbara Jean was even cute then!''

"Yes, we're thankful for such a sweet little girl,'' Sara agreed, "but I still miss my baby.''

"Noah, I'm really worried about Barbara Jean.''

"What's the matter with her?''

"She's just been coughing and coughing. Listen to her breathing. I think she's seriously sick.''

"Do you think I should call the doctor out again?''

"Please do. I don't want to take any risks.''

Noah turned to the phone, his hands shaking. Another sick baby! They had taken her to the doctor on Monday, and Barbara Jean had seemed to improve. Now she was worse again. Barbara Jean hadn't been eating as much as usual since her bout with the flu in December, but she had been quiet and seemingly healthy even with the disrupted routine of the past week in their home. Barbara Jean did have a cold the day of Henry's funeral, but she had been very cheerful. She had waved and said good-bye to almost everyone there. Now the little girl was flushed, feverish, and fussy. And the weather was dreadful, with a cold wind driving the icy snowflakes through the Friday twilight.

"Doctor. . .Noah Beachy calling from Plain City. Our little girl, Barbara Jean, still seems to have a fever, and now she is having a hard time breathing. Would you be able to come out and look at her?"

Mary Lou and Judy came into the room as though drawn by the words on the phone. Now they knew Barbara Jean was really sick. Mommy and Daddy didn't call the doctor often. Mommy hadn't allowed Barbara Jean outside all day, but the little girl had felt well enough to crawl up on the sewing machine and wave to her mother when she went out to do chores. After that she had just whimpered until the folks came back in. Now Mommy was rocking her instead of fixing supper, and Daddy was calling the doctor. The girls knew it was serious.

"What did he say?" Sara's eyes sought Noah's as he finished his conversation.

"He'll be right out."

"Could you make these hungry children some sandwiches while I rock Barbara Jean?" Sara asked. "They must be starving."

Noah complied, and the smell of grilled cheese soon eased the girls' worry and drew Marvin into the room. They had just started their hasty meal when the doctor arrived.

"Nasty weather," he remarked as he

closed the porch door behind him. "So, where's the patient?"

Noah led the brisk doctor into the bedroom, explaining his daughter's symptoms as he went.

The doctor wasted no time. As he listened with the stethoscope, his brow furrowed. "I don't like the sound of that breathing. I think you should take her to the Children's Hospital in Columbus right away. It could be pneumonia, and she would be better off there."

Fear registered in Sara's brown eyes. The Children's Hospital? None of her young family had ever been there before. All five of her children had been born at home with no trouble. Even that summer when Marvin had gotten so sick from gas fumes their doctor had taken care of it.

The picture of that day was etched in Sara's memory. Her young musician was standing on the cultivator hitched to the F-20 and singing into the tractor's gas tank because he "liked the way it sounded." Marvin had sung until he almost passed out before Noah found him and carried him back to the house. When Marvin had come to on the porch, he had been so surprised! They had all laughed afterward, when they knew he was okay. But *this* time the doctor was saying Barbara Jean needed to go to the *hospital*!

"Okay, let's go," Noah took charge of the

situation. "I'll call a driver, and we'll drop the children off at Roy's place."

In a short time the details were taken care of, and Noah, Sara, and the feverish Barbara Jean were on their way to Columbus. Fortunately the snow wasn't piling up yet. Sara was taking no chances. She had wrapped the baby in several blankets and packed an overnight bag. Twenty-five miles was "a-ways" from home, and she wasn't leaving her precious little girl there alone.

The brightly-lit store windows flashed by, but no one spoke. Rasping coughs reminded them all of the seriousness of their errand. Silent prayers went up from each one as they turned in at the hospital in the middle of town.

Noah carried Barbara Jean through the glass doors into the antiseptic emergency room. The scrubbed hospital smell, the sight of women pacing the floor while men smoked nervously, and the sound of doctors being summoned on the intercom unnerved him. Impatiently he answered the receptionist's questions, wishing they would hurry and look at Barbara Jean. Finally an orderly came and wheeled her away to be examined.

"We'll need to have you sign this form yet, Mr. Beachy." The nurse pushed a half-sheet of paper toward him. "They can't treat her until you do."

Noah and Sara read the brief document together.

PERMISSION FOR OPERATION

Date: ___ January 25, 1946 ___

Permission is hereby granted to the
authorities of the Children's Hospital,
Columbus, Ohio, for such procedures as
may be necessary in the case of
___ Barbara Jean Beachy ___
for any medical and surgical procedures
including the giving of anesthetics, which
may be necessary. We will not hold the
hospital responsible in case any contagious
disease is contracted.

WITNESS: [signed] Ferne M. Holmes, R.N.
SIGNED: _____

_____

Grimly Noah signed it.

"Can we go in with the baby?" Sara asked shyly.

"No, you'd better wait out here. They should be out before long."

The minutes dragged by. Their driver had settled down with a magazine until he knew whether a ride home would be needed. Noah fidgeted in his chair. Sara quietly prayed. What were they finding out?

The rattle of stretcher wheels in the hall caught their attention. Was it Barbara Jean? The golden hair confirmed it. Would they have to keep her here overnight?

Noah and Sara stood up to meet the emergency room physician, who, to their surprise, was a woman.

"I think she has pneumonia in the left lung." Dr. Leech answered their unspoken question. "We'll put her in isolation on the second floor. We've given her some sulfides and taken an X-ray. Follow us up to her room."

Sara held the baby's dimpled hand all the way up to her room. She could feel the rapid pulse and noted with dismay a tinge of blue around the lips in Barbara Jean's otherwise pale face. Would she be okay? Sara had often felt this baby was too good to keep, too precious to remain on this sinful earth, but she didn't want her to die! Pneumonia wasn't really serious, was it? Sara clenched her teeth to keep from crying out.

When they got to Room 224, Dr. Leech was all business, ordering an oxygen tent, IV, and medication. "You might as well go home," she told the couple. "Call us in the morning to get a report."

Sara shot a pleading look at Noah. "We don't want to go," he said. "We're prepared to spend the night. We don't want to leave Barbara Jean."

"The hospital has no place for parents to stay," the doctor snapped in her tired voice. "She will be fine. Now go on home and get some rest."

"But . . ."

The doctor sighed impatiently. "We'll let you know if you're needed!"

Wordlessly Noah and Sara kissed the baby and walked out of the room. Behind them they heard Barbara Jean's restless crying. Why couldn't they stay? They wouldn't be any trouble! Even from the sidewalk outside, Sara could hear the little girl's cries. Leaving at that time was heart-rending.

The ride home was a grim one. Fortunately the three older children were sleeping when they picked them up, so no explanations had to be made. With heavy hearts, the parents settled down to a restless night.

Chapter Three

Her condition's unchanged."

The hospital report did little to alleviate the worry in Sara's heart. Mechanically she added to the postcard she was writing to her sister Barbara.[†]

Plain City, Oh

Dear Sisters,

Greetings in Jesus' Holy Name.

How are you folks? Hope fine.

I am just writing a few lines to let you know we took Barbara Jean to the hospital last night for pneumonia. They didn't allow us to stay there. Sure was hard to leave her. We were to the doc. with her Monday. She was better, then Thursday she got worse again. The doc. was out yesterday and said we shall take her as soon as possible to the hospital, so we

[†]All letters and diary entries quoted are authentic. Minor spelling and sentence structure changes have been made for clarity.

did. We want to call the hospital this morning. [later] Report on Barbara this morning is unchanged. Not better nor worse. She had 101.6° fever last night.

Best wishes,
Noah, Sara, and family

I drop a card Monday again.

"Marvin, please run this out to the mailbox for me," Sara called as she pasted on the one-cent stamp.

"But, Mom, it's cold, and the lane is so long!"

"I know, but I want this mailed today so my family knows about Barbara Jean."

"Well, all right."

Sara continued with her Saturday work, but restlessness nagged at her mind. Finally she could stand it no longer. She grabbed her coat and hurried out to the barn.

"Noah, how soon can we go down to Columbus? I just can't stand not being with my little girl!"

"I know what you mean! I'm feeling the same way. I've got the things done that have to be done, so I'll come in, call a driver, and clean up. Maybe you can get the children ready to go to the neighbors."

As Noah and Sara prepared to leave, the phone rang. "Columbus Children's Hospital calling. Is this Noah Beachy?"

"Yes."

"The doctor said you should come down to be with your daughter, Barbara Jean. She's a very sick little girl, and she seems to be getting worse."

"We'll be right down."

Sara knew without asking what the message had been. Uneasiness gripped her anew.

In a short time Noah and Sara found themselves in a small hospital waiting room on the second floor. Although they had made their presence known, no hospital personnel seemed to have any information for them. They sat and waited.

The hours dragged on. What was happening? Pacing didn't help; reading didn't help; they wanted to know about their little girl!

Afternoon wore away to twilight. Supper time came and passed. Neither of them was hungry. Anxiety continued to gnaw at them. "I've had all of this I'm going to take!" declared Noah. "Somebody must know how she is!" Noah went into the hall and stopped a nurse making her rounds. "I'm Barbara Jean Beachy's father, and I want to see her. Where is she?"

Startled, the nurse tried to evade the question. "Hasn't the doctor been in to see you?"

"No."

"I'll get him." The nurse edged away.

Finally the doctor entered the quiet waiting room. "I'm sorry, but your daughter expired this afternoon. The body is in the morgue waiting to be identified."

The color drained from Sara's face. Barbara Jean? In the morgue? No! It couldn't be! Tears choked her voice. "They didn't tell us! They didn't let us see her, and now she's dead!" Sobs shook her small frame. Their precious angel-daughter had been snatched away.

Noah couldn't answer; he was sobbing, too. Wordlessly they followed the doctor down to the morgue where he left them with a receptionist. "She will take care of all the details," he assured them as he walked out.

"Name?" she inquired impersonally.

"Noah Beachy. Here to identify our little girl."

"Come this way."

The nauseating smell of the morgue struck them like a blow. On a brightly-lit white table they saw her—composed and peaceful, with a slight smile on her face. Her flaxen hair was scattered about, showing the restlessness of her last hours.

Spasms of grief gripped the couple as they stared death in the face. Irreversible. Hopeless. The earthly end.

Finally, almost grudgingly, they accepted the

facts. Somehow, *somehow*, it must be the Lord's will.

Their prolonged silence stirred the secretary to action. "What funeral home would you like me to contact?"

"Ferguson—Plain City. When did she die, anyway? Why didn't anyone tell us until now?" Agonized questions burned on Noah's lips.

"They brought her down about three this afternoon. I guess the doctor thought you weren't here. If nobody would have claimed the body soon, they would have cremated it."

"But we were here almost all day!"

"I'm sorry, but I have nothing to do with that part of it." She spun on her white heel and picked up the phone.

"Oh, Noah, how are we going to tell the children?" Tears started again in Sara's eyes.

"We'd better just call and see if one of the neighbor girls can take them home and put them to bed. Then we'll tell them when we get home."

The couple spent ninety cents to send a telegram out to Sara's family with the bitter news. Then they sat down to await Ferguson's hearse. Weariness and spent emotions drained them of all energy.

It was almost midnight by the time they got home, accompanied by the memory of that silent body. Grimly they woke up the children to tell them the sad story. In their half-sleep the youngster's emotions were dulled, but Sara knew it wouldn't be that way in the morning. She dreaded the next day.

The news stunned the county. Noah and Sara had lost another child? Amish church was only held every other Sunday, and this was the off Sunday in their district, but visiting families spread the word. Such a short time after the first one! Hearts of friends ached.

A deep sadness prevailed in the house up the long lane. Marvin, Mary Lou, and Judy wandered about in a daze. "Mommy, Barbara Jean was so good—almost perfect! And she wasn't that sick. Why did she die? Are the rest of us going to die, too?"

Several families stopped by to offer sympathy and encouragement, but it was almost too cold to ride in a buggy to the east edge of the settlement where they lived. The newspapers were calling this the coldest wave of the season, with temperatures dropping near zero. Noah's parents drove over with his sister Betty, his brother John, and John's wife Miriam. John was an ordained minister, and he read the familiar words of John 14 to the grieving family.

"Let not your heart be troubled: ye believe in God, believe also in me. In my Father's house are many mansions; if it were not so I would have told you. I go to prepare a place for you...."

Numbly Sara listened to the words. She knew they were true, but she was bruised and aching. "Why, why?" she cried inwardly. This child was so exceptionally special, and the pain burned within her. And the way she died! Sara had seen the bruises where they had strapped down Barbara Jean, and she knew the last hours had been full of pain. Why should a little child have to suffer like that? The frustration of not being allowed to help when a mother's touch was needed nagged at her mind. Guilt surfaced again. "Maybe I'm being punished for sins of the past," she thought.

Sara looked over to see Noah listening to the Scripture while tears rolled down into his beard. Last week's loss had been hard, but now their grief was multiplied. Sara knew Barbara Jean's niche in Noah's heart would never be filled, no matter how many other children they had. What could replace that cheerful giggle, that trusting hand in his? The aching tightness in her throat refused to go away.

"... And if I go and prepare a place for you, I will come again, and receive you unto myself;

that where I am, there ye may be also."

The promises bathed their sore hearts. God had not forsaken them! Somehow they must believe, they must trust. The young couple knew the reality of pain and yet reached toward God in total trust. God knew their need.

Once again the drafty, bare farmhouse filled with activity. Once again Sara drew on her inner resources and God's help to cope with the three remaining children and details of the funeral. Once again Sara's family paid the fifty dollars to hire a driver and travel out from Indiana to share their grief. Once again that deathly smell punctuated each breath.

Wednesday morning dawned clear and cold. Roy Miller's house was overflowing with people. Somber-faced, the young and old, relatives and friends mingled quietly. They were still in various stages of disbelief. Lots of people lost one child, but to lose two in twelve days? That was a difficult trial!

The singing and sermons really weren't remembered by the young family sitting up front. Everything was a blur to them. The rapid changes, the emotional draining was taking its toll.

The bishop's words penetrated every corner of the packed room. "We've come today to share the grief of Noah and Sara in this difficult time in their lives. It's easy to ask why God would let something like this happen. But God is beyond our understanding. His ways are not necessarily like our ways. His thoughts are far beyond our thoughts. Psalms ninety, verse two says, 'Before the mountains were brought forth, or ever thou hadst formed the earth and the world, even from everlasting to everlasting, thou art God.' God doesn't have to answer to us. Yet we know He is love, and He is holy. Noah, Sara, family, thank God for the precious little girl He gave you. I know she was a joy in your lives as she was to many of us. God will not forsake you now. Psalms ninety-one, verse four says, 'He shall cover thee with His feathers, and under His wings shalt thou trust'. . . ."

Once again the sparkling snow belied the reality of the dark hole in the graveyard. The grieving family was surrounded by loved ones as they once more committed a body back to the dust. Songs about Heaven evaporated in the frosty air.

Lunch was served to the group, and Sara found her sorrow soothed a bit by all the love she felt. These were true friends, and she knew they would help her out in the days ahead.

he dog cried.

Gloom settled over the Beachy household like a heavy blanket, muffling any enjoyment of life. The void was obvious everywhere. The dog, who considered Barbara Jean his best friend, moped about, scorning his food. The three children, restlessly cooped up in the winter-bound house, were trying to understand and deal with the changes in their lives. Not only were the babies missing, but Mommy and Daddy were so sad! Wearily Sara explained again that Henry and Barbara Jean were in Heaven, but she was still sad because she missed them on earth. Accepting this, the children gradually returned to their lively selves.

It wasn't so easy for Sara. Everywhere were reminders of what had been. Grimly she paid the twelve dollar ambulance and embalming fee for Barbara Jean. The $41.20 for the hospital expense would just have to wait a few weeks.

There was no money available right now. Other bills piled up, and Sara knew she would have to help Noah as much as possible so they could be paid. Church members and friends continued to be supportive and helpful, and the grieving family received many letters and cards. Still, they had to face their sorrow individually.

The worst time for Sara was putting away the children's clothes. As she started the task one day, the lines of an old song ran through her thoughts and she sang it softly . . .

Mother, dear come bathe my forehead,
I am growing very weak;
Let the clear and cooling water
Fall upon my burning cheek.
Tell my loving little playmates
That I never more shall play;
Give them all my toys, but, Mother,
Put my little shoes away.
You will do this, won't you, Mother?
Put my little shoes away.
You will do this for me, Mother?
Put my little shoes away.
Now I'm growing tired, dear Mother,
Soon I'll say to you good-day:
Always remember what I told you,
Put my little shoes away. . . .
Mother, soon I'll be with Jesus,
Ere perhaps another day:
Then, oh, then, my loving mother,
Put my little shoes away.

Sara knew these clothes weren't special or fancy, but they had belonged to her cherished babies. Each piece had a memory connected with it. Remember when Henry wore this the first time he went to church? Remember how Barbara Jean would wear this dress as she played gently with the pretty flowers in the garden for hours? She had fit perfectly into that background! Remember when. . . . Sara pressed the worn garments to her face and cried unashamedly.

That night Sara had a beautiful vision. She saw a flower-lined pathway leading to Heaven, and on it a happy, healthy Barbara Jean was smiling and motioning to her mother as if to say, "Come here! Look what I found, Mama." The peacefulness and joy of that special dream calmed and comforted Sara for weeks.

Every day was full of work. To keep the family busy, Sara started her spring cleaning early. All the walls had to be washed free of the smoke from their wood and coal stoves. Windows were washed, shades were wiped, and furniture was moved around to give the house a fresh look. The children pitched in, relieved to find an outlet for their pent-up energy.

As Sara looked around her community with newly-enhanced sensitivity, she saw many needs she could meet. After all, her children were old enough now that she felt a bit more freedom to go and help others. In the middle of this activity, she took time to write her sisters.

March 9, 1946
Plain City

Dear Sisters,

Greetings in Jesus' Holy Name, who had died on the cross for us poor sinners.

We are fine except for colds. Hope this finds you all in good health.

This is a foggy morning, but it isn't very cold. It sure has been warm and nice already the first part of this week.

Wilma, you know Mony Hershberger, the man that worked out here. They had a baby that weighed only 4 ½ pounds, but it was too weak to drink or suck. They fed it with a medicine dropper. Then it got choking spells. Last Sunday it got one (possibly while they weren't with it) and it was passed away when she picked it up to feed. They were away visiting at the time.

I had washed for them since their baby was born because they couldn't get a hired girl. I felt sorry for them. I washed and ironed. I didn't know what to charge, so I said $1.75 a week. I didn't feel that should be too much. I did their washing and cleaning Monday. I wanted to do that free of charge, when I think how much people have done for us! We went to Mony's Monday and stayed there till Tuesday morning. We attended the funeral in the afternoon. It was 26 days old. *The blessed little child! It was nice it could leave this sinful world.*

We were at church Sunday at Dan Helmuths. In the evening we visited Jonas Millers.† *They have a little boy. She sure was hoping for a girl. They now have eight boys and one girl. But they both are getting along fine.*

Wednesday they had a sewing at Alvin Kramers.

We were gone very much the two weeks before this helping people who needed to move. Six families moved from our church. We counted thirty children besides parents, so you can hardly imagine how much smaller the church is. These all moved to Iowa. I do hope they will like it since they have gone, but people felt sorry to see them go as we would have enjoyed having them here to help our church as well. But may God bless them.

We have 500 chicks. We got them Tuesday. They seem pretty hardy so far, although one was dead the other morning.

We saw Henry Yoders when they were here. I talked a long time with her. In the eve we were over to Ira Yoders, then visited a while again....

Say, Wilma, I would like to ask you a question. I wish you would answer on it as soon as you have decided whether you want to or not. Would you work for us beginning October 1 until in December or Christmas?

†The reader may notice that the Amish often used a phrase such as "Joes" or "Joe Millers" when referring to a couple or to a family. Other Dutch expressions may be noted throughout this book in keeping with the culture of the family.

Sara smiled to herself as she wrote that question. Wilma had helped them out last year when Henry was born, and she knew first-hand how lively the children were. Once Wilma and Sara had come in from chores to find Marvin, Mary Lou, and Judy gleefully spreading soda crackers on the floor and crushing them with the rocking chair. Maybe she wouldn't be too excited about coming again!

...With God's help we expect a baby in the last part of October. If we wouldn't have liked you, we wouldn't have asked you back again. Ha! But suit yourself. Let me know so I have time to look around for someone else if you'd rather not work for us.   We were down to the hospital to see what we could find out about little Barbara a few weeks ago. We talked to the head man at the hospital. We got nice satisfaction. We sure miss the children a lot, although we know they're safe on that beautiful shore forevermore. If only we can meet them there some day.

Best wishes,
Noah, Sara, & Children

It is mail man time.
When you can, pray for us. We will do likewise, but in weakness.

P.S. We have received 85 sympathy cards, and from 15 to 20 letters.

Chapter Five

Spring came!

It seemed like a special miracle to the Beachy family when spring came that year! The promise of new life both in the earth and in their home revitalized them.

Eagerly the children helped Sara plant the large garden as soon as the ground was warm enough to work. They wanted to have those fresh, juicy tomatoes as soon as possible! Peas and green beans, onions and radishes pushed through the soil. Potatoes and strawberries, lettuce and sweet corn—the promised abundance was staggering. Of course no garden would be complete without a border of colorful flowers, so zinnias, marigolds, and petunias grew in the garden as well.

Noah began spending long days in the field as spring turned to summer, leaving the chores to Sara and Marvin. Even the girls had their little jobs to do. On exceptionally nice days Sara would pack a picnic lunch, and the whole family would go out and meet Noah in the field. Then they would enjoy the meal together.

Togetherness was something they needed that busy summer. The ordinary tasks of weeding the garden and canning endless rows of colorful vegetables became family projects. The chickens had to be butchered and the meat canned. Everyone was busy.

"We need a break," Noah confided to Melvin Kramer and Ab Miller one day. The three were close friends as well as neighbors and often did things together. "Let's do something special."

"I've got an idea," ventured Melvin. "I just bought that gypsy grocery wagon, you know, that I'm planning to turn into a spring wagon. Why don't we pack up the families and go down to the Columbus zoo? There would be plenty of room for everyone, and I've heard the zoo is an interesting place."

"Super!" agreed Ab. "Let's make it this Saturday. It looks like the weather will be nice and warm."

Sara, Katie Kramer, and Mary Miller liked the idea immediately. "That's just what our children need," Sara thought. "They haven't had nearly enough happy times this year."

It was a jolly bunch that piled into the covered gypsy wagon on Saturday. They took the back roads to Columbus, enjoying the curious looks of passers-by. Soon they had the horses tied up in a shady spot in the woods near the zoo, and the generous picnic lunch was spread. Noah fed the horses (one of his and one of Melvin's) before the families crossed over the dam to go to the zoo.

Excitement ran high as the children oohed and aahed at the animals. Fascinating monkeys, lumbering bears, and colorful birds delighted them all.

Finally, reluctantly, the party turned homeward. Ab regaled them with lively harmonica music, but still the children were asleep by the time they got home. It had been a joyfully tiring day.

By early October it was time for the corn to be shredded. Corn shredding always reminded Sara of the time several years ago when money. had been especially tight. She had dreaded corn shredding that year because she knew there was no money to fix the kind of meal the shredders expected. Those men could attack a meal like locusts, just wiping it out. So what could she do?

Being an ingenious cook, Sara had decided to fix goat meat. Noah bought a nice one at the sale for only two dollars. That meat would go a long way!

When the day came, Sara and a neighbor lady had cooked up a feast of buttered vegetables, snowy mashed potatoes with gravy, pudding made from their plentiful eggs and milk, and fresh apple pie for dessert. The main dish was a savory, seasoned goat-burger meat loaf.

As the noisy, sweaty men tramped onto the porch and washed up at the big tin washtubs, Sara had experienced a moment of trepidation. She knew their neighbor Sam (who was helping with the crew) had often boasted, "Nobody could feed me goat meat; I could smell it." She hoped the spices had done the trick.

After silent prayer the shredders devoured the hearty meal. To Sara's relief, not one person seemed to notice they were eating goat meat. In fact, several of them especially commented on the delicious meatloaf as they helped themselves to more. Sara hid her amusement and decorously kept on serving.

After the meal, one of the foremen did find out what the main dish was, and he laughingly asked Noah, "What shall I do if the men start bleating this afternoon?" Of course, the men couldn't resist telling neighbor Sam about the goat meat he had eaten. It took a long time for him to live that joke down.

Sara smiled. This year, she hoped, their financial situation would be better.

William was born at home October 20, 1946. Judy and Mary Lou fought for the privilege of holding the new baby brother. Eagerly they pointed out to each other his blond hair, blue eyes, and Beachy pug nose. It was about time they had another baby to play with!

Those harvest days were busy ones, but still joy bubbled up in Sara each time she cared for the baby. Although her sister Wilma had not been able to come out to help, Sara managed the extra work. Contentment was the emotion of the day.

One Sunday afternoon the family packed up for a visit to Grandpa Beachy's. Noah's sister Florence and her husband Mark Hochstetler were just back from Civilian Public Service in Warnersville, Pennsylvania. Like many other young Amish and Mennonites, they had served in such work crews during World War II because they were conscientiously opposed to going to war. Now, to welcome Marks back, several of the other brothers and sisters were at the home place as well. It was a lively time of talking, joking, and eating popcorn. The cute baby was admired, but the attention didn't impress him. William fretted and cried most of the time. Sara blamed it on his cold, which she had tried in vain to remedy the past week. Finally they went on home. It really wasn't much fun to visit while tending a fussy baby.

William's cold grew steadily worse. Sara wasn't really worried until Thursday afternoon. Suddenly William seemed desperately sick. His temperature rose to 101^0, and his breathing became a dry, hacking cough. Frantically Noah and Sara called a driver, wrapped up the baby and rushed William to the doctor. His prognosis confirmed their fears. "Take him to Children's Hospital right away."

The trip was marked with dread. Their last experience there had been horrible. Could they help William? Already the anxious parents could see a tinge of blue outlining his lips, ears, and nose. Repressed sobs blocked Sara's throat. Heartbroken but tearless, she clutched the blanketed baby to herself.

The hospital staff was efficient but powerless. Already the little feet and hands were growing cold. Everyone knew death was inevitable.

Hand-in-hand Noah and Sara waited. They had known so much pain in the last year! Now their newest joy was leaving them. Despair and even anger at God threatened to overwhelm them. How could it be? Woodenly they reminded themselves that God was in control, although they couldn't feel it at that moment.

William died at 10:50 p.m., November 21, 1946. The doctor encouraged them to have an autopsy done, since this was the third family death in a year. The resulting diagnosis was grim. Doctor's thought William had a congenital heart disorder called *glycogen storage disease*. This meant that the combination of Noah's and Sara's genes could produce the disease in future children. The disease would enlarge the heart muscles to the point that the child could not breathe properly. William's heart had weighed fifty grams instead of the normal twenty-one. In retrospect, doctors thought it likely that the same disease had also been the cause for Henry's and Barbara Jean's deaths. And there was no known cure. No hope was extended to the family as they left the hospital again with a bill for $5.52 as the only keepsake.

Preparing for another funeral was a dismal experience. Sara moved in a shocked daze. "God, I always thought you were loving and kind. Why are You taking my beloved babies? I can't handle the grief, the hurting. I don't understand! I want to understand; I want to trust You; but I'm overwhelmed with this sorrow. And now they say any more children might have this problem, too. I need Your help! And Marvin, Mary Lou, and Judy are looking to us for stability and comfort. I have nothing to give. I feel like a worn-out, old woman, and I'm just twenty-eight! Only You can provide the healing and strength I need.''

Joe Beachys had church that Sunday morning, and the funeral was held there in the afternoon. Bleak, bare trees and gray skies accentuated the mood. It was a dreary group that surrounded another small grave in the quiet cemetery. This grave would not even be marked by the simple white stone Henry and Barbara Jean had. There was no money available now for anything not absolutely necessary. Noah and Sara wept as they buried another baby.

Chapter Six

Let's play funeral!''

The childish voices carried into Sara's kitchen. Puzzled, she watched the children frolicking in the fresh snow. They were putting Judy's doll into a shoebox and preparing to bury it in a shallow snow-grave. Marvin was obviously the preacher, intoning a blessing over the grave.

Suddenly the suppressed emotions Sara had pent up released themselves in passionate tears. She hurried to her bedroom and fell to her knees beside the bed. In her weeping she didn't hear Judy slip upstairs to get another doll. Uninhibited she cried out, "Oh, God, what can I do? There's nobody around to talk to. Nobody else has lost so many babies. I need Your help, Lord!'' Eventually the tears subsided, and Sara felt the peace of God again.

The Scripture she had read that morning came to her. *"He that dwelleth in the secret place*

of the most High shall abide under the shadow
of the Almighty. I will say of the Lord, He is my
refuge and my fortress, my God; in Him will I
trust. . . . " Psalms 91:1,2.

"I will trust You," she prayed in renewed
commitment. "Give me courage each day. Help
me teach these children about You. My work
ahead is obvious; help me not to look back."

Later Sara copied a poem by an unknown
author and put it in their family Bible.

> *Life is made of volumes three*
> *The past, the present, and yet to be.*
> *The past is done and laid away;*
> *The present we live from day to day;*
> *But the last of these, volume three*
> *Is hidden from sight, and God holds the key.*

Thus resolved, Sara went on with daily life.
Marvin had started school, and Mary Lou and
Judy kept each other occupied. Sara had time
to reminisce about the days when the three were
younger.

Choretime had been an adventurous time for
them. As soon as they were old enough, Sara had
left the three in the house so she could help Noah
with the milking. One evening they came back
in to find all three of the children cowering
behind the couch.

"What's wrong?" Sara asked, concerned.

"There's somebody looking in the window," Mary Lou quavered.

Noah turned to Marvin for clarification.

"We were playing, and we heard a noise on the porch and then on the window. When we looked up, there was this face staring in at us! I think it was just the goat, but it looked like it would break in and maybe hurt somebody . . . ." Marvin tried to explain the fear that had gripped them all.

Only several weeks later Noah and Sara came in to find the three lying on the couch, quieted once more by fear. "What's wrong this time?" they queried.

Timidly little Judy pointed toward the stairway. "The mouse is coming out," she whispered. There was a little nose sticking suspiciously out from under the door, so Noah walked over and opened it. The mouse didn't run, as he had been prepared for it to do. It was already dead!

Marvin had teased the girls unmercifully after that for being scared of a little dead mouse. They were too young to remind him that he had lain on the couch as scared as the rest until the folks came in.

Judy hadn't always been scared of mice, Sara remembered. During the summer months on the Sundays not scheduled for church, the

Amish held Sunday School at the Plainview Christian School building. While there one day, Judy had come back from the outdoor restrooms all excited.

"Look what I found, Mommy," she whispered. "Baby horsies!"

Curiously Sara peeked into the folded handkerchief Judy had thrust onto her lap. Inside were nine hairless baby mice! "Judy," she whispered, choking back laughter, "these are baby mice. They still need their mommy. Run back out and put them where you found them, okay?"

Reluctantly Judy had put them back, not realizing she had just enacted one of the family anecdotes that would be repeated for years to come.

It was difficult to get ready for Christmas that year. Sara wanted to create some happy memories for her brood, but money was tight, and emotions were still tender. Finally a week before Christmas Noah and Sara did their meager shopping. Twilight was falling as they arrived home just in time for chores. Noah hid their purchases in a nearby shed while Sara settled the children in the house. "I'll fix supper as soon as we're done choring," she reminded them. "You just stay in here and play nice."

Marvin could hardly wait until Sara closed the door behind her. "I know where Daddy put the Christmas presents!" he announced proudly. "I saw him carry the bags out to the shed. Let's go look at them."

Mary Lou and Judy considered this novel idea. Those brown bags had been tempting them all the way home from town. Now Mom and Dad were choring, and they would never find out. "Okay, let's go," they told Marvin.

Quickly Marvin got out the flashlight, and they all put on their coats. A quiet but excited trio followed the yellow beam to the shed.

"What is it? What is it?" Judy fairly danced with anticipation as the older two carefully pulled items out of the bags.

"Well, it looks like you girls get dolls this year, and I have a tractor," Marvin decided upon examination.

"Now we'd better get back inside before Mommy and Daddy catch us," worried Mary Lou.

So they hurried back to the house.

From the barn Noah noticed the flickering flashlight trail and guessed immediately what had happened. "That Marvin," he thought. "I'm going to have to teach him a lesson."

Noah believed the Proverb, "Spare the rod, and spoil the child." Marvin learned a lesson that night all right! Never use a flashlight if you want to fool Daddy about where you've been!

The girls learned about Daddy's knack for discovering misbehavior that winter, too.

"Have you ever tried going barefoot in the snow?" Mary Lou asked Judy one day.

"No."

"Well, I think it would be kinda fun. Let's just run around the house once and see what it's like!"

"Okay."

They found out it was very cold, and their spanking after Daddy saw their tracks convinced them not to try that again.

Another afternoon the girls were holding a tea party with their new dolls upstairs in the bedroom. "Okay, now we have to wash dishes," Judy announced. "I'll bring up some water from downstairs."

Mary Lou was surprised at this suggestion. "I don't think Mommy and Daddy would like that, but I guess they'll never find out."

In the bustle of cleaning up their party a movement at the end of the lane caught Mary Lou's attention. "Daddy's back! Hurry up and get rid of that water!"

In her haste Judy knocked the edge of the

table and spilled some water. "How are we gonna clean it up?" she worried.

Resourceful Mary Lou grabbed a large handful of toilet paper, soaked up the water, and threw the sodden mess out the window onto the sloping roof of the porch below. "There, everything looks okay," she whispered.

But Noah saw the paper on the roof and knew something was up. Another paddling for those girls was in order.

Noah found that the occasional goats his family raised were even less easy to keep in order than his children.

One fine spring afternoon the McNess salesman drove up the lane with his car full of cases and boxes of flavorings, linaments, cleaning supplies, and other necessities for his rural customers. While he was talking to Noah and Sara, the three children delightedly watched their small curious goats. One climbed in the open door to investigate the contents of this strange car and nibble the candy on the dash while another clambered on the roof. It was a long time before that salesman came back!

Another proof of the goats' car-climbing expertise came when Eli C. brought over his new maroon Buick for son Noah and the grandchildren to admire. Before anyone noticed it, a goat had climbed onto the hood, leaving small scratches in its wake.

Those goats!

Marvin decided to experiment one day and hitched up a normally docile goat to a pony cart. "Judy, come take a ride," he coaxed.

Judy eyed the contraption with suspicion. "Is this one of your tricks? Am I going to get hurt?"

"No, this is the friendly goat."

"Well, why don't you ride in it?"

"I'm too big! Come on, are you chicken?"

"No!" Judy tried to convince herself.

"Then get in!"

"Okay."

With Judy settled, Marvin lightly switched the goat and watched it take off. When the frightened goat dumped Judy at the edge of the garden, Marvin was quick to comfort her. It had been an interesting experiment, but he didn't want her telling the folks about it!

By the late summer of '47 Sara knew she was expecting another baby. She hid the fact as long as she could because she was afraid to hope. Would this baby be okay? She made necessary preparations, but kept it as simple as possible. She wanted to be ready for the baby, and yet she didn't want to get her heart set on it.

It was a busy winter. Sara continued to help the many people she saw in need around her. Noah's sister Betty was married in December, and his brother Alvin was planning to marry in February, so she spent several days helping her mother-in-law.

Verda was born Sunday, January 24, 1948. Once again the Beachy girls had a cute baby to play with. Marvin was disappointed that the baby wasn't a boy, but soon he adored her as much as the other children did. Automatically the household centered itself around this precious baby.

At six weeks of age Verda developed a bad cold. Instantly the family plunged into despair. These symptoms were all too familiar. Henry, Barbara Jean, William . . . all of them had started out with "colds" only days before their deaths. And now the doctors were saying that there was a family problem with heart disease. Probably it was only a matter of time until Verda too was dead, they feared.

The doctor's orders to take her to Children's Hospital confirmed the family's fears, yet they had no choice. Resignedly Noah and Sara took Verda down to Columbus. She was admitted immediately with a diagnosis of bronchopneumonia.

This time Sara was determined to stay over-night; and their new doctor, Dr. Herman Karrer, encouraged her to do that. Yet as Noah left that evening, they held no hope that this baby would go home with them alive.

It was a long night for Sara. She sat next to the oxygen-tented little girl, holding the dimpled hand. Memories of her other babies paraded through her tired mind. As she prayed and crooned soft nothings to the baby, Sara began to realize there was a difference here. Verda didn't seem to be getting worse. In fact, as morning crept near she actually seemed to be improving! Her breathing was relaxed, her pulse steady, and pink color was tinging the baby cheeks.

The nurse confirmed Sara's intuitive diagnosis. "It looks like a few days in here should get her back as good as new," she assured Sara.

Sudden hope flooded Sara's entire being. "Lord, thank You!" she whispered as she hurried to call home with the good news. Verda was getting better; she would live!

Spring was a happy time. Sara almost enjoyed paying the $100.00 hospital bill. Her baby was well worth it! Verda delighted the family with her antics and accomplishments. At six months she could stand fearlessly in one of Noah's big hands while he raised her to the ceiling. It was a favorite trick he had started with the older children, but Verda was especially adept at it. Yes, life was good again.

Chapter Seven

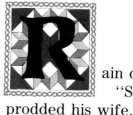ain drummed the roof.

"Sara, it's time to get up," Noah prodded his wife.

"Oh, Noah, I don't feel good. Can you start chores and let me sleep a little longer? Then come back and wake me up."

Noah decided that would be okay for one morning. He knew Sara wasn't feeling well with this latest pregnancy in the summer of 1948. Some extra sleep would be good for her.

"I think I'll call Eli Yutzys and see if I could take the girls down there for the morning. Then you can really rest," he reassured her.

"Okay, but be sure to put a scarf on Verda. She's starting with another cold."

Gratefully Sara stretched out again. It would feel so good to stay in bed! Groggily she heard Noah wake the girls.

A nagging anxiety dogged Noah's steps as he mechanically went about his chores. It was so unusual for Sara to complain about her own aches and pains that he was afraid something was really wrong with her. Finally he went back in the house to check.

"Noah, you'd better call the doctor. This seems serious," Sara told him in a painfully weak voice. She didn't tell him she could almost feel blood draining from her arms, and she was fearful for their unborn child.

Frantically Noah dialed Dr. Karrer.

"I'm sorry, he's not here right now, but I'll try to get a hold of him," Margaret Karrer said. "We'll be over as soon as we can."

"I'll call Dr. Inglemeyer," Noah decided. "I don't think he's as good a doctor, but we need help."

It seemed like an eternity until Dr. Inglemeyer drove in. Noah had piled nine blankets on Sara in a vain attempt to warm her up. She was growing paler all the time.

The doctor walked into the bedroom to examine the patient. After a cursory glance he said, "I'm sorry, I don't think there is anything we can do."

Noah stared at him in disbelief. "You've got to help, Doctor. Can't we take her to the hospital? You must do something!" Despair gripped him.

Just then Dr. Karrer and his wife-nurse

Margaret came rushing in, bringing their equipment along. A quick examination showed them the gravity of the situation, and they sprang into action.

"Call the ambulances—both of them," Dr. Karrer ordered. "Whoever gets here first will take her in. Margaret, the saline solution."

His order was unnecessary. Margaret had seen many transfusions during World War II and she already had the precious glass bottle in hand. She had only one, but that should be enough. Quickly she set up the IV, clamping it to the white-painted, high metal headboard. The needle was in place, the bottle ready to connect. Clang! In her haste the bottle hit against the metal. Her heart sank. If that bottle was broken she knew Sara would die. But—it wasn't! Thankfully she set up the saline solution, hoping against hope that they weren't already too late. With a sigh of relief she watched the essential fluid drip through the tube into the depleted veins.

Somehow Noah found time to call neighbor Melvin Kramer. Melvin scribbled a note to his wife and came immediately. He took in the situation at a glance and pitched in to help. "Marvin and I will take care of the rest of the chores. You don't have to worry about a thing at home," he assured Noah.

The Ferguson ambulance won the race up the long lane and backed up to the door. In a matter of seconds they had bundled off the now-unconscious woman. Out the drive they flew! The driver, Charles Jay Ferguson, looked back to check Sara and Dr. Karrer just gestured commandingly—DRIVE!

Sirens wailed. From the neighbor's living room Judy heard the sound with terror in her heart. Tears rolled down her cheeks, and she refused to be comforted. In a small rocker she sat looking at a Bible storybook picture of angels. She was afraid that her precious mommy was now an angel. On and on she cried.

Noah sat silent and grim-faced holding the cold white hand of his wife. They had shared a lot of sorrow, but it had been *together*. Now if he lost her, he didn't know how he could handle it. "Would that driver speed up?" he muttered. A glance at the speedometer showed they were already going 90 mph. The hum of the tires became a prayer. "Let her live, let her live, Your will be done, but please let her live."

Meanwhile Dr. Karrer fought for Sara's life. At the edge of Columbus, the police escort Margaret had called for met them. They needed all the help they could get!

The ambulance screeched in at the hospital they could reach first in Columbus, the White

Cross. Straight through the operating doors they wheeled her, but the attending doctors pushed the stretcher right back out. "This woman is dead."

"She is *not* dead!" Dr. Karrer pushed her back in authoritatively. "Get busy!!"

"Noah, I think she'll live." Dr. Karrer's face was haggard, yet relaxed. "It was a tubal pregnancy that ruptured. She lost about seven pints of blood, some of which we were able to transfuse back into her during surgery. It will take a long time to recover her strength, but she'll live."

"Thank the Lord!"

It was one happy family that was reunited several weeks later. The near-tragedy had reminded them of just how essential Sara was to the family. Neighbors had provided delicious food and regular transportation to the hospital. Aunt Christena and others had taken care of baby Verda. Sara's family had butchered a beef for them. Their needs had been met, yet there was no one like Mother to give encouragement and keep things running smoothly. Even the disappointment of missing the trip to Indiana for Aunt Wilma's August wedding paled in the face of what could easily have been. Mommy was home!!

Chapter Eight

hibbee-go-sheep!''
Twilight calls of children at play
provided a pleasant background for the adult's
chatter. Al Helmuths, Melvin Kramers, Ab
Millers, and Noah Beachys enjoyed their fre-
quent evenings together, often playing Sorry,
Rook, or throwing horseshoes. Tonight the men
had played with the children awhile, but now
they were on the porch cranking the well-worn
ice cream freezer.

"This ice cream just won't freeze tonight,''
Al complained, rubbing his sore right arm.

Just then his wife Amanda called from the
door, "Hey, if you men want some ice cream,
we need the canister to put the mix in!''

Sheepishly the men gave her the cold,
recently-cranked canister. "All that work for
nothing!'' they groaned.

Companionably they discussed the latest
venture, trash hauling. Ab would drive Melvin

and Noah to sales where they would buy old metal parts at a low price. They could haul a truckload of scrap to Columbus and sell it for a tidy profit. Along the way they often enjoyed Pepsi and filled up on seven cent White Castle hamburgers.

The women, meanwhile, were busy talking as they worked on their embroidery and other handwork projects. "Rachel Miller said she will work for us this fall when the baby is born," Sara confided. "I've heard she's a good worker."

"Yes, she is, but if you need any more help just let us know!"

By September 16th, 1949, everything was ready for baby Howard's arrival. Noah had called the doctor out to the house, and Rachel was there to assist in any way she could. There was guarded joy surrounding this baby. As Judy sadly put it, "When there is a baby, I just expect another funeral."

Sara didn't let the uncertainty keep her spirits down. She often told the children, "I know you have plenty of work to do, but why don't you just drop everything and come listen to this Bible story while I iron."

Those were precious times for the children.

They would gather around and listen as Sara made familiar Bible stories come alive in the re-telling. They learned the awesomeness of God's power and the depth of His love. They could feel that God was very real to their mommy. She even told them how she had heard the voice of God audibly calling her name one day. She knew He cared about her personally. He had spared her life, and so she told the children that He cared about them, too.

Sara passed her tranquility of spirit on to others. Rachel's struggles with teenage problems and questions about Scriptures and joining church were easily expressed to Sara, and she gave her wise counsel. Sara made clear to Rachel that the way to be saved was to trust in Jesus Christ, and to let His blood atone for her sins. She explained that being baptized and following all the rules of the Amish church in a sincere attempt to obey the Scriptures was important, but she could not *earn* her salvation. It was still an undeserved gift.

There was lots of work to do in the Beachy household. By now Mary Lou and Judy were old enough to help with simple tasks, but dawdling seemed more to their liking. Rachel found it necessary to paddle them for their pokiness, but they still considered her a kind and loving "maud."

When Sara's dad Henry died only four days after Howard's birth, Noah and Marvin went to Indiana for the funeral. It was unseasonably cold. Marvin's reaction when he returned was negative. "No, I didn't have a good trip. I couldn't understand what was going on, and everyone was so sad. It's even worse when a grown-up dies than it is for babies!"

Several weeks later Rachel was helping with the chores when Sara came out with a phone message for her. "You'd better go to the hospital right away," she said. "Your dad's been hurt in a farm accident, and they want you to come."

That left Sara to do all the work again, since Rachel needed to stay home and care for her father. Soon Sara's normal efficiency re-asserted itself. She knew how to make the dust and dishes fly.

As baby Howard grew, so did the family's attachment to him. Still, the occasional bluish tinge around his mouth and fingernails warned that all was not well. In late October Noah and Sara finally took the baby to the Children's Hospital for an X-ray to see if his heart was enlarged as William's had been.

The next night Sara was trying to get back to sleep after Howard's restless, sickly cry finally quieted in slumber. She was afraid this would be another case of losing a baby, and it was so hard to face. Suddenly she jerked awake. Something in the room had changed. There was a mysterious light in the room! Looking fearfully toward the cradle, Sara saw the softly glowing wings of an angel hovering over the sleeping child, and then silently it left through a window. She blinked her eyes for a better look, but the angel was gone, and so, she knew, was baby Howard. She rose to check.

Yes, Howard died November 1, 1949. The inevitable sorrow was easier on Sara this time because the vision of the angel had reassured her that her little one went to be with God. She felt new strength to deal with the grief of the rest of the family as the small unmarked grave joined the row in the cemetery.

Sara held fast to her vision of the angel as consolation. Although she shared the vision with the family, she cautioned the children not to tell anyone else. People wouldn't understand. To them Sara would seem to be either bragging or going crazy with grief. Privately Sara knew this wasn't the case. In His love, God reached down to send her a special message. She was loved! God did care about her and her unusual family. In spite of the trials she faced, Sara knew God was in control.

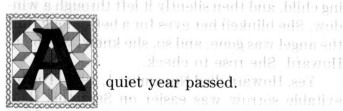

quiet year passed.

Dear Sister,   *March 16, 1951*

Greetings in Jesus' Holy Name. We are all fine except Verda does not seem to feel so good since we are at home. [They had visited Indiana the past weekend.]

Our 350 chicks are supposed to come this morning. We aren't raising too many broilers—just pullets.

We came home about 7:30. We had to wait 3½ hours in Lima. We could have had it nice if we would have taken the 9:20 bus.

It was raining all the way to Lima, and from there it was snow. It's snowing this morning again. We can't shred for a while if it keeps this up and doesn't freeze.

The fires were out when we came home. Of course, it was not unexpected for us since the choreboy wasn't too old and neither is Marvin. They had a good time anyway.

I don't think I'll wash, or not too much this week. I'll get a start next week. Best wishes. I want to write to Mother also.   *Noahs*

*P.S. I happened to get Edna Mae's dollie and book along.
I'll send it out as soon as I get to it.*

Sara sighed to herself as she finished the short letter. The fire hadn't been the only thing Marvin neglected. Her pet, a yellow canary, had starved to death as well. Marvin had been so sorry and apologetic, but. . . . "I guess he will grow up soon," she reminded herself.

Noah and Sara worked their hardest, but farming still wasn't a very profitable venture for them. When the old Pearl Price farm became available in Resaka, southwest of Plain City, they decided it would be best to move. Their friends, Ab Millers, had already moved over and seemed to like the area.

It was a big, rambling, old farmhouse with rough wooden floors, but Sara soon made it a home. Maybe things would get better at last! The baby girl born there on November 19, 1951, made it seem like a fresh, new beginning. (She was one of five Beachy grandchildren born that fall. Uncles Alvin and Jonas as well as Aunts Anna [Christner] and Florence [Hostetler] were also blessed with new babies.)

"What shall we name this baby?" Noah asked the older children.

Delighted with the prospect of picking a name, Mary Lou and Judy considered various possibilities. Finally they settled on "Miriam." Their Uncle John's wife was named Miriam, and she was much admired by the girls. Besides, the name sounded elegant.

"Miriam it is," decided Noah and Sara. They were so happy with this dark-haired baby! She had a perfectly-formed round face, and a dark curl caressed her forehead.

Many of their friends came over to visit and see the baby. Sara's nephew Omer Slabaugh and his wife Marie came to visit also, carrying their young son Ernie, all bundled up because of the cold. As they were unwrapping the little "cocoon," they suddenly exploded with laughter. They had been carrying poor little Ernie upside down! Sara joined in the laughter. This irrepressible nephew of hers had a cheerful attitude toward life that was positively contagious. Yes, friends and family were at the top of the list of blessings this Thanksgiving season.

The bubble burst December 13th. "Mommy, look at Miriam! Whenever she cries her face turns blue," Mary Lou observed.

Sara's heart sank. To her that simple statement meant only one thing. Miriam was going to die.

After consulting Dr. Karrer, Miriam was admitted to the Children's Hospital the next day. Her cynosis was so pronounced that she was diagnosed as being in cardiac failure. With Digitoxin, oxygen, and lots of fluids she seemed to improve. During her stay, doctors took a small sample of muscle tissue. They wanted to see if the *glycogen storage disease* they suspected as the cause of the other deaths was present in Miriam. They did find some glycogen present in the muscle, but at that time couldn't tell if it was an abnormal amount.

Just in time for Christmas, Miriam came home to be with her family. Mary Lou and Judy spent lots of time rocking the baby. They even wore a face mask to protect her from germs. Sara slipped away long enough to go to the older children's program at school, but found she needed to spend much time with Miriam.

After New Year's Day, she wrote to Barbara on a penny postcard:

Dear Sister,

Greetings in Jesus' holy name. I'm ashamed I didn't answer your welcome letter. I don't know how to thank you enough for the box of things. You have done so much already! It made me feel kind of guilty to use all the nice things. We have snow and it is pretty cold.

We brought the baby to the hospital last night. The doctor gave her very little hope. She has the heart ailment. They're doing what they can. She is blue and very weak since her last shot. I'm trying to get a hold of Noah. He left at 7:00 a.m.

I'll end with love to all. Miriam is sleeping. I hope she sleeps right on and need not suffer more on earth if she can't get well.

Pray for us,
Noahs

P.S. Miriam seems a little better this afternoon.

January 8th Sara was up all night. Miriam could take very little milk, and in the morning their neighbor, Ed Miller, took them to the hospital. Miriam was in obvious distress. Her pitiful crying made the way to the Children's Hospital seem endless.

The trip was in vain. By the time Ed got home, Noah had called again. "Could you come up and get us again? The baby just died."

Sara recorded her feelings in the privacy of her diary.

Jan. 9, '52 Wed. Took Miriam to the hospital. She had great pain, cried hard, and died at 9:00. Sad was the hour, but safe was her soul. Came home about 2:00. Soon many people came.

Jan. 10, '52 Thurs. Many people were here. Showed respectful sympathy. We find ourselves very small and little done for people compared to what was done for us.

Jan. 11, '52 Fri. Was sweet little Miriam's funeral. 2 carloads came from Indiana. Had funeral at Joe Detweilers. Buried in New Cemetery with the other 4 loving children.

For Sara's niece, Edna Mae Troyer, these baby funerals were a new experience. "Why is there such a big hole for such a little box?" she asked innocently.

Sara echoed the question in her heart. How could such a little girl leave such a big hole in her life?

oah's still in bed.''

Sara sipped her tea thoughtfully as she pored over her diary. This was becoming repetitious and worrisome. Noah had been sick off and on all spring and summer. The doctors didn't exactly know what was wrong. The common term was ''colitis,'' but no treatments seemed to be effective.

Sara had her own explanation for the ''colitis.'' She felt Noah was simply reacting to all the stress he was under. He was such a private person, and all the emotions aroused by the loss of five children in the last six years had been buried inside. The strain of worry and the humiliation of poverty were taking their toll, she felt. Only God could really solve his problems.

Financially things were getting worse. They had been staggered by Miriam's $244.58 hospital bill. Even meeting the $15.00 monthly payment was hard. On one of their trips to Indiana, Sara confided in her sister Wilma. "I have to be so careful when I buy groceries. Our children get hungry for things and beg for things just like other people's children, but I can't afford Kool-Aid and things like that. I can't even buy fresh fruits and vegetables to help my children stay healthy. It's so frustrating!"

It was hard to accept all the help that was given, even though the givers had the best intentions. Yet without that help the Beachys would never have made it. Neighbors came and helped plow, plant, and chore. A sister bought linoleum for the kitchen and helped put it in. Later Sara found a poem by an unknown author that helped her keep a proper perspective about money. It said:

> *Money will buy a bed, but not sleep.*
> *Money will buy books, but not brains.*
> *Money will buy food, but not appetite.*
> *Money will buy a house, but not a home.*
> *Money will buy medicine, but not health.*
> *Money will buy amusement, but not happiness.*
> *Money will buy a church, but not Heaven.*

Other people helped by just being friends. One evening Omer Slabaughs came over and had everyone laughing until two a.m. with the "Bean Chair" stories Omer could tell. These stories were originally Pennsylvania Dutch letters printed in the *Middleburg* [Pennsylvania] *Post* in the late 1800's and signed by "Gottlieb Boonasteil." They were satirical pieces written by Thomas Hess Harter, attempting to encourage social reform through ridicule. Because they were so humorous, they were told simply as stories by later generations. The old tales featured such characters as Bean Chair and his wife Polly, Mike Penny-Pincher, Mony Rat-Tail and the hired girl, Six-foot Betz. That evening Omer told one of the favorites, the story of Bean Chair and the matchbox:

Bean Chair got up in the morning to start the fire, and he went downstairs in his long underwear. It was dark, and he reached for the box of matches. Polly, his wife, had bought one of these fancy ten cent matchboxes that fall off the wall when you look at it, and as he reached for it, it fell off the wall and he groped around on the floor on his knees looking for this matchbox until his knees were like a wood rasp and covered with goose pimples.

And so it just entered his mind how the Indians used to start a fire with a piece of flint, so he got the old "shrotflint" [shotgun] off the wall and put the powder in. He put the wood in the stove and set the gun on and pointed it in the stove to start the fire. It just went "poosh," but nothing happened. By that time he was "wunder bar" cold, which is just extremely cold, so he just let the gunpowder run into the gun for quite a while. (It was an old muzzle-loader, and at that time they called them flints because they used a flint to set them off.) Well, Bean Chair pointed that gun in the stove, and he set the thing off, and it went "WHOOF!" and stove lids flew around the kitchen like wasps. There were enough ashes on the floor like a real nice rabbit snow that you go out tracking rabbits in.

The neighbors heard the shot and came swarming over like bees. About this time Polly opened the window and shouted, "The Bean Chair shot himself!"

Before they knew it, even the town constable was there. He was about ready to arrest Bean Chair and take him to the asylum when Bean Chair showed the crowd the match box. That settled the business. All the men were immediately on his side. They said any woman who buys one of those fancy match boxes and hangs it up when she could buy a good metal one for three cents doesn't have much sense and should have to wake up and start the fire herself.

It is said that the storekeeper sold over three dozen metal match boxes the next week to people in that neighborhood. The men can now get up any time of the night and get a match without wrecking the whole house.

In spite of distractions like friendly story-telling, Noah was still sick. One neighbor didn't think Noah would live much longer, so he talked to Noah's landlord about renting the farm.

"You don't know the Beachys," Sara thought to herself when she heard that. "They don't give up." Sara didn't give up either. She raised chickens, did butchering, kept the house in order, even helped relatives as best she could.

She comforted Marvin and Judy after each was severely bitten by the neighbor's vicious dog. (Although that dog had earlier saved some children from a mad bull, he was shot after the second biting incident.)

Sara was the one who noticed Marvin's dirty ears one morning on the way to church. "Didn't you wash your ears this morning?" she asked, a frown creasing her forehead. "You can't go to church like that! We're going past Eli Hochstetler's. Run in and ask them for a wet soapy washcloth. Maybe this will help you remember next time!"

It was also Sara's duty to encourage the children in their work at Plain View Christian School. None of them liked school, and they often found the work difficult. A familiar concern was expressed by Sara. "Marvin, I know you really enjoy drawing cars, but you're going to have to spend more time on your lessons!"

1952 was the year of the polio epidemic. For weeks the Amish didn't have church to avoid spreading the dread disease. Even when services were resumed, children were not allowed to attend at first. Thankfully, polio didn't hit the Beachy children. "The Lord knows how much we can handle!" Sara reminded herself.

Although the older children had many responsibilities, they found time for fun, too. Marvin discovered the challenge of motors and rigged up a go-cart on which his cousin John Henry lost two front teeth.

The children also made friends with Paul Christner, who sometimes stayed with them when Noah and Sara traveled. Paul always seemed to have spending money, which made him an instant hero with the Beachy bunch.

"Let's go to the general store and buy some candy," he suggested to Marvin one day.

"Sure, let's go," Marvin agreed.

Off they went on horseback. Gleefully they bought as much candy as they could stuff in their pockets and took off for home to enjoy it.

"Wait a minute! Where did all the candy go?" Marvin asked, dismayed at finding his pockets almost empty when they reached the house.

"Hey, mine's gone, too!" Paul discovered. "It must have fallen out during that wild ride!"

Upon retracing their route, the boys found their candy scattered on the ground. Surprisingly the squashed treats still tasted delicious!

"So much has changed this year," Sara thought to herself one evening as she packed boxes for yet another move. "Melvin Kramer's baby died in July. Noah's brother Eli and his family moved to Cleveland. Crist and Christena have gone to Florida for the winter. Omers had a new baby and spent a lot of time in the hospital with their older son Ernie after he hurt his head. At least Noah's feeling better! Now with this move to his folks' 'old home place,' we'll be on a really good farm with a modern milking set-up and a system to grow fresh oat sprouts continuously for the cattle. We can be a real help to his folks there, and maybe things will start going better for us again."

Sara couldn't let her latest pregnancy slow her pace. December 4th was moving day, and they got settled in the small house next to Eli C's. Since there was a lot of corn-husking left to do at the old place, Sara helped.

"Noah, I think the time has come to go to the hospital," Sara said after a full day of husking corn.

Noah didn't waste any time. Because of their previous problems, they had decided this child would be born in a hospital. Noah called a driver, and they arrived at the Marysville Hospital just twenty minutes before Wilma Irene, 7 lb. 6 oz., was born on December 15, 1952.

Once again a cautious optimism was felt by the Beachy family. For the moment they ignored the depressing family-history note Dr. Karrer had filed in his medical report for the Marysville Hospital. *"Five of these apparently normal children have died between the ages of 6 wks. and two years of age within a few hours of having contracted a mild upper respiratory ailment. [Three]. . .died in acute cardiac failure at Children's Hospital. Autopsy findings revealed only a glycogen defect in heart muscles."*

By the time Christmas shopping and programs and family get-togethers were over, Sara was worn out and needed to relax. But January 3rd, Wilma got sick and was admitted to Columbus Children's Hospital. Sara stayed with her there through the oxygen, EKG's, medication, and X-rays. When they left for home January 8th, Sara knew little Wilma wasn't hers to keep either. "We'll love you while you're here," she whispered to the reddish-brown-haired bundle in her arms.

Sara tried to shield the rest of the family from her inner conviction that Wilma would not live. Marvin discovered her secret one day when he saw tears rolling down Sara's cheeks as she rocked the baby.

"Is the baby sick, Mommy?" he asked.

Sara tried to brush away her tears without him noticing, but she knew that now he also knew what was happening.

Meanwhile Eli C. and Mary Ann had left for a winter in Florida. While they were away, Noahs could live in the bigger farm house instead of the small dawdy house they were used to. Sara, her niece Verna (the "maud" for this baby), and the girls ambitiously cleaned Eli's big house and moved the family belongings over for several months. The room to stretch felt wonderful!

Although Wilma kept growing and developing almost normally, Sara never felt at ease. A treatment in nearby Marion didn't help, and finally on January 23rd Noah and Sara took Wilma to the Children's Hospital again. Wilma had been short of breath since the afternoon before, and her color was getting worse.

It was a dreary, rainy winter day. Sara's thoughts kept returning to the Ben B. Miller family, whose son Edwin had died from a blood clot. That funeral was to be today, and she knew just what they were going through.

Holding back her tears, Sara waited as Wilma underwent more tests and treatments. She didn't need a medical expert to tell her that a pulse of

200 and a breathing rate of 112 respirations per minute was a serious condition. The X-rays showed Wilma's heart was enlarged even more than it had been. Doctors gave her morphine and oxygen and tried to get her to drink some juice with little success. It just wasn't the same as her normal formula of Carnation milk with Karo and water.

The day dragged on. Finally close to ten p.m. Noah and Sara left Room 450 for a short break. While they were gone, Wilma stopped breathing. Nurse Harris rushed to the station. "We need artificial respiration, NOW!" she ordered.

Dr. Beridge stepped in quickly, but it was in vain. "I'm sorry; she has expired," he told the couple when they returned.

Once again Noah signed an autopsy permit. Their five-week-old baby had a heart three times normal size and even an enlarged spleen. Grimly they turned the body over to Paul Ferguson. Now going home meant another funeral.

Sara cried all the way home. "I hope people don't pray that we have any more children," she sobbed. "It hurts too much. You love them, take care of them, and then they're gone. Is it really fair? We have to trust God; I know we have to trust God, but why are all these things happening to us?"

"Oh, Lord, I don't have enough strength!

Help me through this sad hour. Thank you that dear little Wilma is now healthy with You, but comfort us now I pray.''

Numbness settled over Sara like a cloak, propelling her through the appropriate motions. Verna had the house all cleaned up, and relatives and friends flocked in. Late Sunday evening Eli C's and Crist and Christena pulled in from Florida. Ab Miller's wife Mary made a beautiful white dress for Wilma to be buried in.

The young folks came and sang. *"Oh, come, angel band; Come and around me stand..."* Sara's sore heart drank in the comforting words. *"Oh, bear me away on your snowy wings, to my immortal home."* Wilma had reached that safe and happy home already. Praise God only her body was in that casket!

The funeral was held at the "old home place." It was the first time Noahs had lived in a place big enough to hold the funeral there. Sim Yoder, Eli Nissly, and Noah Troyer preached the sermons. A strong, cold wind seemed to drive the hurt even deeper into the aching Beachy family. One more hope was lost.

The *Plain City Advocate* carried a cold and bleak front page obituary on January 28, 1953.

INFANT DAUGHTER DIES IN HOSPITAL

Wilma Irene Beachy, age 1 month and 8 days, infant

daughter of Mr. and Mrs. Noah Beachy of Canaan Township died in Children's Hospital in Columbus, Friday, January 23.

Services were held at the home Monday afternoon, burial in the Amish Cemetery.

Chapter Eleven

'm so tired!''

Sara allowed herself one day of rest and retrospection after the funeral before venting her frustration on any dirt in sight. Her mother, Mary Hochstetler, stayed in Ohio for a month to help out. They cleaned the house from top to bottom again, washing bedding, waxing floors. The lawn was raked, and even the brooder house was cleaned.

Sara and her mother also did a lot of visiting during this time with local friends and relatives. Gradually Sara found the pain easing away and the scars healing again.

Spring brought Sara's favorite kind of weather. She enjoyed starting her tomato plants inside and then setting them out in the freshly-plowed garden. She delighted in the outdoors. With the older children in school, she also found time to help neighbors move or paint or get ready for church or whatever there was to be done.

As a special treat Noah took the children to the Ohio Caverns in April. Cleaning the attic in solitude gave Sara the time she needed to think through her life again. Quietly she recommitted herself to God and to her family.

Early in May the summer pace began. Eli C. and Mary Ann came back from Florida, so Noahs moved into the small house again. The children were released from school, and farming became a full-time occupation for them all. As Noah and Marvin worked in the fields, Sara, Mary Lou, Judy, and Verda tended the garden. They froze and canned all sorts of vegetables for the inevitable winter.

For some time now Noah and Sara had been struggling with their membership in the Old Order Amish church. Many of their friends had already left, and it seemed as if the people at the Canaan Beachy Amish Church were more spiritual and mission-minded. Since Noah's parents were with the Conservative Mennonites, he found it easier than Sara did to make the change. Sara was reluctant because she had been taught to be loyal to the Amish church. Yet she knew that now her first duty was to her husband rather than to her parents. It was with sadness, and yet with the underlying consciousness that they were doing the right thing that Noah and Sara joined the Canaan church in June, 1953.

Fourteen-year-old Marvin thought it was pretty exciting when Noah brought home the '41 Chevy that was their first car. "I'm gonna drive it!" he announced.

"First of all we practice," Noah stated firmly.

An empty field proved the perfect training ground. Together father and son learned how to handle this new convenience.

August 10th was a special day for the extended Beachy family. For the first time since 1945 all Eli C's children were at home together! They had attended a larger Beachy reunion, and then enjoyed the evening at the "old home place." Ice cream was served to celebrate before they scattered across the United States again.

The rest of 1953 went by fairly quietly. Noah started driving the school bus for extra income. The Beachy house was often full of company— friends for a meal, or relatives overnight. Sara enjoyed cooking and with the help of her daughters always spread an ample table. The family visited relatives in Indiana several times. A garage was built onto the small house. Much butchering was done, including canning meat for the Mennonite Central Committee's world relief program. On November 4th, Noah's grandfather, Cornelius Beachy, died at 91 after a long and fruitful life. Melvin Mullet and

Emmanuel Mullet preached the sermons at his funeral.

David Jay came into the world November 20, 1954. Once again everything seemed normal. However, one doctor scribbled a warning note on the baby's chart: *"Watch vital signs in baby, and if any cynosis develops, put in incubator."*

Nothing happened. Sara's empty arms were suddenly full again with a lively baby who chewed on his fingers. Verna again lent her capable help as a "maud," and the rest of the family pitched in gladly. Sara still hesitated, though. Did she dare hope again?

Chapter Twelve

He's so cute!''

Mary Lou, Judy, and Verda oohed and aahed at 7-month-old David. He was going to Aunt Lena's wedding, and in celebration of the occasion he had graduated from the traditional Amish baby dress to his first pair of pants. Marvin didn't say much, but Sara could tell from the glint in his eye and the camera in his hand how proud he was of this baby brother. Tears welled in her eyes as she thought of the happiness David had brought into their home. He was so marvellously healthy! At two months he had had a case of whooping cough (along with his big brother), but since then he was doing very well.

It was a gorgeous June day. Large vases of peonies colored each window in the rambling farmhouse as Lena Beachy became the bride of Norman Yutzy. She was the last of Eli C's children to marry, and Eli squeezed Mary Ann's hand as they witnessed the solemn occasion.

Sara smiled to watch her in-laws. They were always so kind and affectionate to each other. "How does it feel to have all your children gone?" she wondered. "They tried hard to raise them right." Sara couldn't foresee that eventually four sons, one daughter, and two of Eli's sons-in-law would become ministers.

"RING! RING! RING!"

The insistent ringing of the telephone jarred Noah from a sound sleep.

"Hello."

"Noah? I'm afraid I have bad news for you. There's been a house fire at Simon Slabaughs. Three of his sons lost their lives. Susie and the other children are in shock, but okay. Would you please drive over and break the news to their son Omer and his wife Marie?"

"Oh no," Noah breathed. "Of course we'll tell them. And we'll start out for Indiana right away."

Sara looked questioningly at Noah as he hung up the phone. "What happened?" she asked wide-eyed.

As he explained, Sara began crying. "Poor Susie! Oh, my poor, dear sister. Let's get out there right away!''

As Noah dressed, they planned. He would drive over and tell Omer the news. Omer's sister Barbara was staying with them, too. Both of them would be grief-stricken. Sara would pack and make arrangements for the children to come out the next day. Marvin was out of school now. He could handle things on the farm.

When the carload arrived in Nappanee, they stopped first at Sara's sister Wilma's place to change clothes. Then they learned the full story. The fire had started in the heating stove. Simon had escaped with Susie and some of the children; but when he heard the screams of Glenn (10), Simon Jr. (9), and Larry (5), he felt compelled to go back and try to rescue them. The attempt failed, and Simon died with his sons. The older children, Martha and John Henry, also tried to use a ladder to reach the upstairs bedroom, but were unsuccessful. Tearfully Noah and the family drove out to view the tragic scene. The fire was still smoldering, and bluish flames marked where the bodies of the four victims still lay.

"AMISH FATHER AND THREE OF HIS THIRTEEN CHILDREN PERISH IN FARM FIRE" the headline of the Nov. 2, 1955 *Goshen News* blazoned. Hundreds of friends, relatives, and church members flocked in to help with the clean-up and comforting. The sorrow was indescribable. Sara's tears mingled with Susie's as they embraced. So often Susie had been a comfort to Sara. Now their roles were reversed.

"We just can't always understand the way God works," Sara counseled. "Go ahead and cry, but keep trusting. God does still care about you. You will feel it later on."

Life did go on.

Paul Allen was born on blustery January 12, 1956. He weighed 9 lbs., 12 oz., and his heart rate and rhythm seemed to be normal. Still the doctors were cautious. They put on his records, *"6 brothers and sisters have died of Von Gierken disease (glycogen storage of the heart). This baby will be watched carefully."*

What a fussy baby! Paul cried most of his first night at home, and that was just the beginning. His continual fussing concerned Sara, and they even took him to the hospital once to have his heart tested. There were no abnormalities, and eventually he grew through the fussy stage.

As Paul started to smile and captivate his parents' heart, life took on new meaning for Noah and Sara. They grieved with their friends, Monroe & Lizzie Ann Kurtz, when they had a second stillborn son that February. Seeing him buried so close to the Beachy babies made Noahs realize anew how precious their little boys were.

Sara also enjoyed watching the development of individual personalities as her children grew. Marvin was almost grown-up. His main worries seemed to be keeping his Studebaker Starlite Coupe spit-polished and playing guitar. Mary Lou and Judy were becoming vivacious young ladies, who seemed to be always surrounded by friends. Now Noah and Sara often found their house occupied by giggling girls for a slumber party or a youth group for a social. Verda was the in-between one. She was sent on all sorts of errands, teased by the older ones, and often partially responsible for the younger ones. Verda was such a perfectionist that her sisters often said she didn't play with her toys—she only rearranged them. She was also a spunky little girl who knew how to "hold her own" in a squabble.

"Dear God, thank You for this wonderful, precious family," Sara often prayed. "Help me to enjoy each moment with them and to raise them to serve You."

ere's a blond one!''

Sara smiled at her husband from her hospital bed in familiar Room 55. This had been her room for the last three children, and it held many happy memories. "This one is Noah, Jr., I think!''

"Well, I guess if you insist. . .'' Noah hesitated. Sara had suggested that name before, but this might be the last time to use it. He wrote the name on the birth certificate. The other children were waiting in the car to take home this small baby that had been born April 5, 1957. The birth certificate was the last formality to complete.

"Excuse me,'' their old friend Margaret Karrer looked up from her nursing chart and interrupted them. "I know this is none of my business, but think about that child's future. There are so many Amish and Mennonite boys named Junior! He will get everyone else's mail and have all kinds of trouble. Can't you think of a more original name?'' The nurse's face was flushed at her own boldness, but she felt strongly about this issue.

"You do have a point there,'' Noah admitted. "What do you think, Sara?''

"Well, I guess I'll leave it up to you and the other children. If you can think of a name that suits everyone, I guess it's okay with me. But I would like a 'Junior,' too.''

Noah went out to the parking lot and held a quick conference. They settled on 'Robert Gene,' and so that was the baby's name. Since there was another Robert in church, this baby was soon called Gene.

Gene was slightly blue at birth, so the hospital staff had whisked him into an incubator and provided extra oxygen. Soon his color was normal, and when he went home from the hospital two days later, he appeared to be in excellent health.

Then life changed at the Beachys! As the three boys grew, they found more and more mischief to get into. After all, there were three minds to think up escapades!

One of their favorite tricks was letting the milk truck run over their small toy cars and trucks. They would leave the toys on the milk truck's path and watch the destruction. Then they would run complaining to Mommy and Daddy and beg for new toys.

When they were confined to Grandpa Beachy's big house in the winter, the boys loved to run through the circle made by the doorways connecting the kitchen, dining room, and living room. With their toy tractor, cars, and chairs they soon wore a dark track into the floor while filling the house with laughter.

That house had several other advantages as well. A large stairway flanked with banisters was great for sliding and jumping. The clothes-chute from the upper level was frequently used for toy transport. And—when Mommy and Daddy weren't looking—the attic held treasures of all sorts. Grandma Mary Ann's fancy old dresses and other memorabilia of a bygone day fascinated the young Beachys. Who needed expensive toys and the best of everything when they had their imaginations and each other!

Two years later, January 29, 1959, LaVern joined the family. This time Marvin wasn't at home to celebrate. He had gone to a six-week Bible School in Berlin, Ohio. As Noahs brought the baby home, Sara marveled anew at the miracle of life. After losing six babies, having four healthy little boys was a special blessing.

In May Marvin, Mary Lou, and Judy decided to go to their church youth meetings in Iowa.
Their only hesitation about going was that
LaVern was still suffering from a two-week-old
cold. The fear that had been hidden and almost
forgotten for so long came back full force. What
if something happened to LaVern while they
were gone? ''What do you think, Mom? Should
we go or not?'' Marvin asked.

''I think you should just go. It will be a good
experience for you,'' Sara said. ''We'll take care
of LaVern the best we can. I just don't know
what to expect with him. You can call home
every day to see how he is.''

Marvin breathed a sigh of relief. This trip
was especially important to him because he was
picking up Amy Miller in Goshen, Indiana, and
taking her along to the meetings. They had been
writing to each other since Bible School, and he
had been eagerly anticipating spending the
whole weekend with her. Her friendly person-
ality, sparkling brown eyes, and sensitivity to
others made her a joy to be around.

The meetings were exciting and inspira-
tional. Amy wanted to introduce Marvin to some
of her relatives in that community, and Mary Lou
and Judy soon found friends to enjoy the
weekend with.

Friday evening Marvin and Amy went to one of her relatives for supper. When they rejoined the youth group, they found Mary Lou and Judy in tears. "What's wrong?" they asked, immediately concerned.

"LaVern is in the hospital," Judy informed them. "He had trouble breathing, and they took him in this morning. I just know he's going to die now," she went on tearfully. "It seems the children always do if they get sick enough to go to the hospital."

"I'm afraid of that, too," Mary Lou added. "How soon can we leave for home, Marvin?"

"Get your things together after the meeting tonight. We'll sleep a couple of hours and then take off," Marvin decided.

Meanwhile Noah and Sara were keeping watch at LaVern's hospital bed. They knew the latest X-rays had shown a grossly enlarged heart. The doctors said he was in "moderately severe" cardiac failure. It was only a matter of time.

The older children arrived Saturday afternoon. Grimly they gathered around the hospital bed and said their farewells to the littlest brother.

When LaVern died at three p.m. Sunday, Sara sighed and bit her lip to hold back her cry of anguish. It had been six years since Wilma's death, and she had almost started taking healthy babies for granted. Now chubby LaVern was gone. From deep within, the tears came.

An autopsy report didn't answer many questions. The *glycogen storage disease* assumed to cause the deaths of the earlier babies wasn't evident at all. Now the doctors were suggesting *myocardial fibroblastosis*.

"Why can't the doctors do something to help?" Sara agonized to herself. "They've just watched my children die and can't seem to solve the problem at all. It's totally frustrating!"

Once again the dreary business of preparing for a funeral began, and the sickly-sweet smell of embalming fluids filled the house. Sara pulled a piece of soft white fabric from her cupboard and asked two young girls, Mary Troyer and Sarah Gingerich, to make the funeral dress. They wanted to help, but this made death so real and personal to them that it was a very difficult task. "Now we can understand a little bit more what Mary Lou and Judy have had to deal with so often!" they whispered to each other. "How can they take it so well?"

When the body was dressed, the family solemnly gathered together in the front room. In the small casket they saw a tiny body reposing peacefully in a simple white dress. "He looks just like an angel," Marvin breathed.

Both the *Columbus Dispatch* and the

Columbus Citizen carried a terse, distorted version of the news in the hospital columns of the May 11th editions. "**BEACHY,** Laverne, 3 months, daughter of Mr., Mrs. Noah Beachy, of Plain City, May 10, Children's." The *Plain City Advocate* again saw this as front page news. In the May 13th edition they printed this:

PLAIN CITY BABY, LAVERN BEACHY, DIED SUNDAY, 10th Lavern [sic] Beachy, age 3 months, of Plain City RFD 1, died Sunday at Children's Hospital in Columbus.

Survived by parents, Mr. and Mrs. Noah E. Beachy, 3 sisters, Mary Lou, Judith Ann and Verda; 4 brothers, Marvin, David, Paul and Robert Gene, all at home.

Funeral services were held at 9 a.m. Wednesday, May 13th at the home of the parents, the Rev. Elton [Eldon] Troyer and the Rev. Raymond Kauffman officiating.

Interment in Canaan Amish Mennonite Cemetery by Charles Jay Ferguson.

The house was crowded for the funeral. Marvin's friend Amy had asked Uncle Jonas Hochstetler's about a ride out from Goshen, and came with some of Marvin's cousins. It was just before the funeral that she met Noah and the surprisingly young-looking Sara for the first time. Taking her place beside Marvin, Amy self-consciously joined the family for the service.

For the little boys this funeral was a new experience, and they didn't know exactly how to act. Instinctively they sensed the solemnity and were very quiet.

Going to the graveyard was the most difficult part for Sara this time. In direct contradiction to the spring of new life in the air, they were laying away another precious baby.

There were two rows of babies here by now; seven of theirs, three of Monroe Kurtz's, and several others from their church. This new grave would not have a stone either. They just couldn't afford one. As tears rolled down her cheeks, Sara suddenly felt old—old and very tired. "Oh, Lord, haven't we had enough sorrow? Help me through, I pray. I know You have before; please help me now."

Chapter Fourteen

She said, 'Yes'!"

"Judy, would you like to be one of our witnesses? Mary Lou, would you help serve at the wedding? And Verda, would you carry gifts?" Marvin asked his sisters after a weekend in Indiana. Amy had consented to marry him, and he was eagerly making plans.

"Well, we're real happy for you," Noah spoke for himself and Sara. "Marriage is a big responsibility, but it is also a joy. You've picked a real nice girl. I'm sure you'll be happy."

Marvin nodded his head in agreement. "One bad thing is that we'll be living in Indiana, but that's not too far away. I think we'll move a trailer up close to her folks. It seems like there are plenty of construction jobs out there, so it should be easy to get work."

"We'll miss you," Sara said quietly.

That winter Noah and Sara were able to take Verda, David, Paul, and Gene to Sarasota, Florida to visit Eli C's. It was a big adventure for all of them, highlighted by seeing wild hogs and riding a work horse at a park. They especially remembered this horse because Verda, the boys, and a stranger all rode it at once. The ride was great; but when they dismounted, the stranger ended up in the water trough!

In January, Marvin moved to Indiana to start his new job. Without the help of his oldest son, Noah found the chores noticeably heavier, and Mary Lou and Judy had to pitch in. Even the German shepherd collie, Rex, didn't cooperate as well with Marvin gone. Marvin had trained the dog to get the cows on his own without human supervision. But try as he might, Noah couldn't make that dog fetch the cows! So he had to get them himself.

Paul also had a special friendship with Rex. The two would go out ''rabbit-hunting'' by the hour, even though Paul was too young to take a gun along. One day they were gone so long that the family grew concerned. It was almost dark. Where were they? Only when Noah climbed up and looked out a haymow window did he see the two scampering in the woods. When the anxious father reached his son, Paul nonchalantly explained, "We were having fun running the rabbits."

With spring came the bustle of preparing for Marvin's wedding. Each of the girls had a new dress— yellow for Verda, pink for Judy, and green for Mary Lou. Sara even made a dark blue one for herself. Sewing was a task she didn't really enjoy, but she had learned through necessity to sew quickly and neatly.

It was a Friday evening when they arrived in Goshen. They toured the 10′ X 50′ trailer set up by Amy's folks and helped the nervous couple finish up the wedding details. Sara admired the gray rose pattern of the china Marvin had given Amy as she carefully washed it and arranged the dishes in the cupboards. She prayed God's blessing on the couple as she worked.

Sara thought Marvin and Amy's simple wedding ceremony at Pleasant Grove Conservative Mennonite Church on Sunday, April 10, 1960 was beautiful. The afternoon sun lit the church, highlighting the soft pastels of the women's dresses contrasted with the men's dark suits. A few tears of happiness blurred the lovely scene. "Ah, my strong, handsome, oldest son!" she thought. "What a joy he's been to us! It does seem he's plenty young to get married. We even had to sign for his marriage license! But I guess we were even younger. How thankful I am that he's serving God and has picked a Godly companion. I hope they won't need to go through as many rough times as we have, but we will trust the future to God.''

Exactly a year later Marvin and Amy brought Catherine Rose home from the hospital. ''How does it feel to be a grandpa at forty-one?'' Marvin teased his dad.

''I think it feels pretty good!'' Noah boomed over the phone. ''Is everything okay?''

''Everyone's fine! The baby's got lots of dark hair and big blue eyes. You'll have to come see her.''

And come see her they did! Right away the new Grandma and Grandpa brought out Aunt Mary Lou to help with the baby. Then every month it seemed either they had to come to Goshen or Marvins went to Plain City. Noah and Sara were seriously thinking about moving to Indiana, so they also went farm-hunting frequently. It would be so nice if they could live near Sara's family as well as their son and his family.

It was while Noahs were on one of those trips

to Indiana that Mary Lou and Judy found out a joke can backfire. They decided to take David, Paul, and Gene to the Dairy Queen one evening. On the way, Mary Lou began tapping the gas pedal erratically to make it sound as though the engine was "missing." "There's something wrong with the car!" she exclaimed.

"We must be running out of gas," Judy agreed readily.

Soon the jerking of the car wasn't enough to keep the boys worried. Mary Lou swerved back and forth on the road and . . . oh dear! . . . landed in the ditch. Besides hitting her head on the mirror, it was humiliating to have nearby Eli Hochstetler pull the car out. All for a joke! And by then the Dairy Queen was closed!

Chapter Fifteen

ut I'm a grandmother!''
Sara was rather dismayed when
she discovered she was expecting another child.
Somehow she had assumed LaVern would be the
last. The older she got, the harder it was to make
all the adjustments of pregnancy. And it seemed
this time she was just continuously tired. One
flight of stairs could leave her breathless.

Finally in September, Dr. Karrer insisted that
she enter the University Hospital in Columbus.
''I don't like the sound of your pulse, and you
tire too easily. Your ankles have been swelling
too much as well. I want you to get a thorough
check-up.''

So Sara went to the hospital. This time she
didn't worry much about things at home. The
girls were very capable of handling those details.
Only Verda and David were in school right now,
and the other boys were old enough that they
no longer demanded constant attention.

For three weeks Sara went through various tests. Doctors removed a small piece of muscle to see if she might have adult *glycogen storage disease*, but she didn't. They took an electrocardiogram and gave her a cardiac fluoroscopy. When she went home September 30, 1961, all the doctors could tell her was that she had some sort of undiagnosed heart disease.

"You just take it real easy," they advised.

With Dr. Karrer they were much more specific. Dr. Ryan wrote him a letter:

Dear Doctor Karrer:

This is just a follow-up note to our conversation regarding Mrs. Beachy. That she was in cardiac failure was quite apparent, but as I said previously, I have no idea what kind of heart disease she has. I am sure it must be related to the fact that she has had seven children [with] supposed glycogen storage disease. The only thing we came up with was the physical findings and symptomology of heart failure as you did with gallop rhythm and tachycardia. She had left bundle branch block on her electrocardiograms. She seemed to be approximately 4 1/2 months pregnant. Her admission weight was 138 lbs. and her weight at discharge was 130....She seemed to be improved at the time of discharge, but for the three weeks she was here she was very inactive. As I said

over the phone, she walked out in the hall
one evening and [had] a little nocturnal
dyspnea that night. She wished to go home,
and I can't say as I blame her. We dis-
charged her to you on digoxin 1/4 mg b.i.d.,
hydrochlorothiazide 50 mg b.i.d. and a 2 gr
sodium diet. You may have to add mercurate
at whatever interval you think necessary to
keep her at a steady dry weight. After our
telephone conversation, I spoke with Dr.
Copeland and he would be only too happy to
deliver Mrs. Beachy at term. We should see
her in about 2 weeks, I think. As I said,
she may have to spend the last month in the
hospital. I am not sure that she realizes
how sick she is, and I don't believe that
her husband as yet appreciates this fact.
She should be quite inactive around home now
because the load of pregnancy begins to pick
up, reaching its peak at about three weeks
only to return at the time of labor.

We certainly enjoyed seeing and taking
care of this very pleasant and very interesting lady. I wish we had an answer as to
what type of heart disease this is. Feel
free to call us at any time.

> Best regards,
> [signed]
> Joseph M. Ryan, M.D.

That fall Noah and Sara found a farm to rent near Emmatown, Indiana. Sara was excited because this would mean living close to her brother Jerome as well as to her widowed mother. The family could move in January. Hopefully in a year or two they would then be able to buy a farm out there.

"January?!" Judy wailed. "How can we move in January? Andy and I want to get married in April!"

"That's easy, Judy," her dad told her. "Just move out with us, have the wedding out there, and then move back."

"Da-a-a-d! I don't want to do that! All our friends are here. His family all live around here, and we don't know what the church will be like in Indiana! Besides, I have to be here to get our trailer ready!"

"Judy, maybe you could move your wedding date up and get married here before we move," Sara suggested.

"We'll talk about it," Judy promised.

"But remember," Noah said firmly, "your mother will need help with this move. No matter when the wedding is, we'll be expecting your help when we move."

"Okay, Dad."

December 12, 1961, Sara went into the hospital to wait for the new baby's arrival. It was hard to lay there day after day knowing that Judy was working on wedding plans (with Mary Lou's help, of course), and Noah was preparing for the move. At least the cows had been sold, so the chores were lighter. To make the time go faster, Sara worked on a piece of embroidery for her granddaughter. "Now I lay me down to sleep...." The pastel figures and cross-stitch letters soon filled the canvas as she stitched day by day.

As she rested, Sara also spent much time communing with God, seeking strength for what was ahead. She knew she needed inner peace that only He could give to sustain her through the changes of a new baby, a daughter's wedding, and moving to a new home. With His strength as an inner support, she could meet the demands that faced her. She prayed for Noah in his responsibilities as well. And then she prayed for each of the children, that they would choose to follow God and be faithful to Him. She asked that they would not be bitter about the losses of their siblings and the poverty of their childhood. After all, God had taken care of them; their needs had been met. She prayed for victories in specific struggles she knew each one was facing. After leaving her cares in the

Heavenly Father's hands, she could relax. Each time the family came to visit, they found a cheerful, encouraging mother who was very much the heart of their home.

Finally, on December 24, Sharon Sue was born. She was a fragile-looking baby, and the family instantly fell in love with her. She was their Christmas bundle. Marvin and his family came out again to share the holidays, and even though Sara and the baby were in the hospital, it was a festive time.

At two days of age, Sharon Sue had several "cynotic episodes" where her lips and fingernails turned markedly blue. Reluctantly the family transferred the baby to the Children's Hospital for treatment.

There X-rays revealed that the little girl's heart was already enlarged, but a muscle biopsy did not show *glycogen storage disease*. Doctors kept her in the hospital two weeks, but reached no conclusion. A frustrated doctor scrawled on her chart "*. . . the nature of the heart disease is still undiagnosed, but is probably not glycogenosis. 'Idiopathic myocardiopathy,' whatever that is, is a remote possibility.*"

Sharon Sue came home to a house full of escalating busyness. Judy was sewing for the wedding, and Mary Lou finished up her job in town. The girls and Sara packed belongings and thoroughly cleaned the house while Noah cleaned the shop and attended to business details. January 6th there was company to celebrate Old Christmas (Epiphany) and to see the baby. A group of neighbors brought in ice cream and cake along with a gift of lawn chairs for a surprise farewell. Their kindness touched Noah and Sara. How they would miss these friends!

On Wednesday, January 17th, Marvin and Amy brought out a load of relatives to help prepare for the wedding and the move. Somehow in between the work, Sara found time to write these descriptive diary entries:

Jan. 17, '62, Wed. Had a lot of help. Baked sheet cakes. Marvins, Susie, Sylvia, and Barbara came for dinner. Potatoes were cooked in jackets. Ironing was finished. It was a cold day. Noah, Marvin and Omer took a load of furniture to Indiana. Came back a little late that evening.

Jan. 18, '62, Thurs. Had plenty of help. Cooked potatoes. Baked a few cakes yet. Frosted all sheet cakes. Noah and Marvin and I went to Columbus to get plates, cups, napkins, ice cream, and all things for the wedding. Sharon was brauf [well-behaved]. It was cold! Floors were scrubbed and porches. Got Christena in Columbus at 4:30 in the morning at airport. Wayne came along.

Jan. 19, '62, Fri. Had plenty of help. Made sloppy joe (28 lbs) Cooked tapioca for pudding. Finished the wedding cake. [It was decorated by Sylvia, wife of Sara's brother Ed.] Cleaned the rest of the house. Set up wedding tables and set them. Had plenty of help. Also cut up celery and cooked eggs.

Jan. 20, '62, Sat. Judith and Andrew Gingerich married today. The sun shone and there were snow flurries part time. Was a beautiful day! Pretty cold. Had close to 300 for dinner. Received a nice variety of gifts. In the evening were between 50 and 70 for supper. Everything was pretty well guessed in eats. Some potato salad and cake left. Joe Dans had Sharon Sue.

The *Plain City Advocate* reported the wedding in the January 24th edition:

BEACHY-GINGERICH VOWS SPOKEN

On Saturday, Jan. 20, at the Canaan A.M. Church, Bishop Steve Yoder of Nappanee, Ind., officiated at the marriage of Miss Judith Beachy, daughter of Mr. and Mrs. Noah E. Beachy, and Mr. Andrew Gingerich, son of Mr. and Mrs. Jonas Gingerich. The attendants were Miss Mary Lou Beachy, sister of the bride, Mr. Ervin Troyer, and Mr. and Mrs. Lester Gingerich. A reception for between two and three hundred from Ohio, Indiana, and Florida, was held at the home of the bride's parents. The young couple will live in a house-trailer near the home of the groom's parents. Mr. Gingerich is employed at the Dobb's-Evans Paper Company in Columbus.

Mr. and Mrs. Noah E. Beachy and family moved this week to Emmatown, Indiana, where he will be engaged in farming.

In the aftermath of the wedding, Sara's sister Susie took Sharon Sue along back to Indiana. At first she didn't want to because it was obvious to everyone that Sharon Sue wasn't very healthy. "What if something happens to her while she's with me?" Susie asked anxiously.

"Sharon Sue is in God's hands. If it's her time to go, she will go, whether she's with me or you," Sara reminded her sister. "I'd just feel better if she wasn't in all the cold air and commotion around here."

With lots of help (including Judy's!), Noah and the family moved to Indiana on Tuesday. Sara wrote:

Jan. 23, '62, Tues. Was cold. Moved from Ohio to Indiana. Started at 4:00, got here at 10:25. Ate dinner at Mothers. Levis and Marvins brought supper in. Everything was unloaded by 3:00. Trucks left for home [driven by] Eldon Troyer, Eli Hochstetler, Melvin Miller, and Noah Gingerich. Was cold and icy.

Jan. 24, '62, Wed. All the sisters and wives were here and brought dinner in. Helped clean and straighten up. Hung more curtains. Enjoyed the day. Susie brought Sharon along over. She was a good baby...

After Noahs took Christena back to the Indianapolis airport, the family tried to settle into a new routine. But Sharon Sue was sick. Only six days after the move Noah and Sara took her to Marvin's trailer, carrying her on a pillow to ease the baby's discomfort. "What doctor should we go to?" they asked.

Amy recommended Dr. Troyer, who immediately sent them to the Goshen General Hospital, where Sharon Sue was put under oxygen. Although she improved at first, her heart couldn't hold out, and she died at 8:30 p.m. on January 29th. The next day the *Goshen News* reported:

SHARON SUE BEACHY

Sharon Sue Beachy, five-week-old daughter of Mr. and Mrs. Noah Beachy, Route 1, Topeka, died about 8:30 p.m. Monday at the Goshen General Hospital. The child had been ill since birth of a heart ailment and was admitted at the hospital Monday noon.

Sharon Sue was born Dec. 24, last, at Plain City, Ohio, and moved with her parents to the Topeka community about a week ago. Surviving, in addition to the parents, are four brothers, Marvin Ray, Route 1 Topeka [sic], David, Paul and Robert, all at home; three sisters, Mrs. Andrew (Judith) Gingerich, Plain City, Ohio, and Mary Lou and Verda, both at home; and the grandparents, Mr. and Mrs. Eli C. Beachy, Plain City, Ohio, and Mrs. Levi Mast, Route 1, Topeka.

Friends will be received after 7 p.m. today at the family home near Emma. Funeral services will be held Wednesday at 1:30 p.m. at the Fair Haven Conservative [sic] Mennonite Church, east of Goshen, with burial in the nearby cemetery. Bishop David Bontrager will officiate. The Miller-Yoder Funeral Home at Middlebury is in charge of arrangements.

Sadly Sara caressed the lifeless body of her last baby. Exactly three years ago LaVern had been born, and he had died, too. So much sadness for one family! Her heart wept once more.

Ladies from the Fair Haven Church made a dress and covering for the tiny baby. The young folks came and sang at the house. On Noah's forty-second birthday, they buried Sharon Sue in a cold and windy graveyard two hundred miles away from the graves of her brothers and sisters back in Plain City. Holding back tears, the young folks sang the familiar Fanny Crosby hymn again:

Safe in the arms of Jesus, Safe on His gentle breast
There by his love o'er-shaded, Sweetly my soul shall rest.
Hark 'tis the voice of angels, Borne in a song to me,
Over the fields of glory, Over the jasper sea...
Safe in the arms of Jesus, Safe on His gentle breast,
There by his love o'er-shaded, Sweetly my soul shall rest.

Safe in the arms of Jesus, Safe from corroding care,
Safe from the world's temptations, Sin cannot harm me
  there.
Free from the blight of sorrow, Free from my doubts and
  fears;
Only a few more trials, Only a few more tears...
Safe in the arms of Jesus, Safe on His gentle breast,
There by His love o'er-shaded, Sweetly my soul shall rest.

Jesus my heart's dear refuge, Jesus has died for me;
Firm on the Rock of Ages, Ever my trust shall be.
Here let me wait with patience, Wait till the night is o'er;
Wait till I see the morning Break on the golden shore...
Safe in the arms of Jesus, Safe on His gentle breast,
There by his love o'er-shaded, Sweetly my soul shall rest.

It was over.

"*Safe in the arms of Jesus....*" The words
kept repeating themselves over and over in
Sara's mind as the days passed. "Oh, dear God,
thank You that our darling baby is safe with You.
Thank You for all the children You have given
us to love and hold. I especially thank You for
those You have spared, and the joy they have
brought to our lives. Thank You for giving us
strength during the many times of sorrow.
Through it all You have been faithful—even
when we couldn't understand. We still don't

understand, but we trust You, Lord.''

Resolutely Sara put the sorrows behind her. It was a new day. A new era of grandmotherhood beckoned ahead. New friends were to be made in Indiana. New adjustments would come, but she knew God would be faithful. She could walk into the future unafraid, cherishing each moment He gave her. God would keep His promises!

Epilogue

Many changes came through the years, but Noah and Sara remained faithful to the Lord. Sara died January 23, 1978, and the following tribute was read at her funeral:

MEMORIAL TO MOTHER

Sara (Hochstetler) Beachy, daughter of Henry C. and Mary Hochstetler was born July 1, 1918; went to be with Jesus on January 23, 1978, age 59 years, 6 months, and 22 days.

Married to Noah E. Beachy, March 26, 1939. Lived in matrimony 38 years, 9 months, 27 days. To this union were born 15 children.

Surviving is her husband, 4 sons, and 3 daughters; Marvin, Goshen; Mrs. Larry (Mary Lou) Flowers, Ligonier; Mrs. Andrew (Judith) Gingerich, Plain City, Ohio; Mrs. Ervin (Verda) Miller, and David, both of Middlebury; Paul and Gene, both at home. Thirteen grandchildren mourn Grandma's passing.

Also surviving are 3 sisters and 1 brother; Mrs. Levi (Barbara) Troyer, Middlebury; Mrs. Crist (Christena) Bontrager, Sarasota, Florida; Jonas, Nappanee; and Mrs. Omer (Wilma) Hochstetler, Milford. Also 8 step-brothers and 3 step-sisters.

Preceding her in death were 4 sons and 4 daughters, all of whom died in their infancy of a congenital heart disease. Five of these preceded their mother in the same month and one on the same day in 1953.

Mother's passing was the third in her family within the past 11 months; her mother on March 20, 1977 and a sister on December 10, 1977.

Mother's heart condition worsened within the past year, and she suffered a stroke on Saturday morning, January 7, while in Sarasota, Florida. One of her sons read Psalms 23 to her, and at the end of the reading she requested Psalm 91. Later that morning from her hospital bed, she expressed her desire to be anointed. Bro. Lester Gingerich officiated at this service along with Harvey Miller, John F. Miller and the family present. Her response immediately following the anointing was "Praise the Lord!"

In the days following her stroke, Mother's mind was alert and she was able to talk with family and friends. At her request, several of the grandchildren were permitted to come up to her room and sing several songs. One of the sons also sang a couple of her favorite songs. On Friday morning, January 20 she suffered a cardiac arrest. Her heart was revived again, but she never regained full consciousness and early on Monday, January 23, she went on to be with the Lord. All of the family was at the hospital with the exception of one who had been there earlier.

The family wishes to express their gratefulness
to friends and neighbors for their kindness and
prayers. The cards and letters received during
her illness were deeply appreciated. May God
richly bless all of you for your expressions of love
to us.

Her sister Wilma wrote these lines:
"Loving memories, sister Sara dear,
Hours thrice blessed when you were near.
Everyone loved you;
Your kindness lives on;
Hoping a white gown and crown were
yours at the Throne."

In November of 1978 Noah married widow
Lizzie Ann Kurtz, who kept him from being too
lonely as the children continued to grow up and
leave home. At the time of this writing the
original family includes eighteen grandchildren
and thirteen great-grandchildren.

Thankfully none of these descendents have
experienced the same kind of heart problems the
eight babies had. Dr. Annemarie Sommer from
the Columbus Children's Hospital did a study on
the family in 1971 and printed the results in *The
Cardiovascular Series*, "Birth Defects: Original
Article Series," Vol. VIII, No. 5, August, 1972.

In a 1986 personal interview with the

author, Dr. Sommer expressed continued interest in the family. She also said that if those children were born today, heart transplants would probably be the only solution to the *idiopathic nonobstructive cardiomyopathy* they suffered from.

Also in 1986, the family purchased five more gravestones to mark the resting places of their siblings in the barren Plain City cemetery, and decided to chronicle the story for others to read. All of us have learned from the experiences of the past what a precious blessing a family is. We know that we must *"hold them near while they're here, and don't wait for tomorrow to look back and wish for today."* [†]

[†] "We Have This Moment Today." Words by Gloria Gaither. Music by William J. Gaither.

1997

 1998

The Family Record

of

Noah E. Beachy & Sara (Hochstetler) Beachy

January 31, 1920   July 1, 1918 - January 23, 1978

Children

Name	Birth	Death
Marvin Ray	October 22, 1939	
Mary Lou	December 5, 1940	
Judith Ann	April 25, 1942	
Barbara Jean	April 4, 1944	d. January 26, 1946
Henry N.	October 5, 1945	d. January 14, 1946
William N.	October 20, 1946	d. November 21, 1946
Verda	January 24, 1948	
Howard N.	September 16, 1949	d. November 1, 1949
Miriam N.	November 19, 1951	d. January 9, 1952
Wilma Irene	December 15, 1952	d. January 23, 1953
David Jay	November 20, 1954	
Paul Allen	January 12, 1956	
Robert Gene	April 5, 1957	
LaVern N.	January 29, 1959	d. May 10, 1959
Sharon Sue	December 24, 1961	d. January 29, 1962

About the Author

Catherine (Beachy) Yoder lives in New Paris, Indiana with her husband Kenton and their young son David.

Majoring in elementary education, she graduated from Grace College in 1984 with a bachelor's degree. She taught fifth and sixth grades at Clinton Christian School in Goshen, Indiana.

Homemaking is her primary occupation, along with helping in the family business of producing model toy tractors for collectors. She also is involved in her church and volunteer work.

Hold Them Near is her first book-length work. Personal memories of a special grandmother and a desire to preserve this story for the benefit of others, along with family encouragement, were the motivation and inspiration for this book.

Special Notes

The cover photograph was taken by Marvin Beachy, and is the house the Beachys lived in when the story began. Marvin took the slide several years ago, not realizing the house was soon to be demolished. The next time the family drove by to see it, all that remained was the weed-covered stone foundation. How thankful they are for this picture!

The quilt block design illuminating the initial letter of each chapter is adapted from a doll quilt Sara made for the author and her sister. The quilt, in solid pastels—aqua, pink, yellow, and white—is special because Sara usually left the quilt-piecing to her sister Barbara, preferring to use her own creative energies on embroidery.

Yesterday and the Present

Each of the seven surviving children was asked to look back on their childhood and reflect on how the events of the past influenced their adult lives. Here are their answers, along with a glimpse of their lives today.

MARVIN is well-known in Conservative Mennonite circles as the founder and director of the Gospel Echoes Team, a prison ministry based in Goshen, Indiana. Through singing, teaching, and distributing Bibles and Bible Study Courses, the team ministers to thousands of inmates each year. Marvin also operates a recording studio in his home. He previously owned a cabinet shop and a bus conversion business. Looking back, he feels the hard times the family went through were good for him, because he learned to appreciate life more. Marvin and Amy have four children and three grandchildren.

MARY LOU lives in Cromwell, Indiana. Besides working in a factory, she puts her floral design training to work by arranging flowers for many weddings and other special occasions. Twice widowed, she found that while raising her three children she was constantly on the lookout for health problems, and thanking God when the children were normal. She feels that because of her childhood, she loved her own children more, even to the point of being overprotective. Now she is enjoying her five grandchildren. Mary Lou notes that the Beachy family is unusually close because of all they went through. They love and appreciate each other, and avoid the petty fighting that divides so many families.

JUDY still lives in Plain City, Ohio with her husband Andy. All four of their children and two grandchildren live in the Plain City area as well. She works as a seamstress and in a fabric shop, while Andy works in a hardware store. Looking back, Judy says what stands out to her is the quality of faith she saw in her mother. Sara was patient, loving, and giving even while going through hardships, and she was always grateful for whatever blessings they had. Judy feels the example she saw of her mother never getting bitter has helped her to avoid bitterness in the trials she has faced as an adult.

VERDA is currently working for her brother Gene in his cabinet shop. As a widow with two sons, she often thinks back to her growing up years. Because of her unique birth position in the family (in the middle of six children who died), she grew up extremely fast. The rest of the family was almost too busy coping with their own grief to meet her needs as a child. Now she says that experience has given her an understanding of the hurts of people, and an extra sensitivity to their needs. With her children and grandchildren she is learning to be open about feelings and to develop close relationships in spite of the potential of being hurt.

DAVID lives in Middlebury, Indiana with his wife Suetta and their two young children. He owns Ultra Body Shop in Goshen, which keeps him very busy. Being one of the younger children in the family, David feels he was spared some of the hurts and sorrows the older children went through. Fifteen years the junior of Marvin, as the first surviving son, David may have even been a little favored. At the time of his birth, his parents were fairly well adjusted to their lot in life, and financially things were a bit more under control. As an adult, David noticed that he was very concerned before his children were born about whether they would be healthy or not, and thankful when they were okay.

PAUL also lives in the Middlebury area. After many years in shipping, he now drives a truck for a living. He thanks God for the family he grew up in, especially for his wonderful mother. He says he learned a lot from his parents, and it was a good experience. Without the trials they went through, Paul feels his brothers and sisters would not be as special as they are.

GENE owns and operates RC Country Cupboards near Goshen, Indiana with his wife Carol. As the "baby" in the family, he is looking forward to Heaven, where he will meet the brothers and sisters he never really knew here. He says that all that happened to their family has made him aware of how much we should value our families while we have them. This awareness of life means it is important to be what we ought to be *now*, and also to spend quality time with our children. His two sons and a daughter are reaping the benefits of that philosophy.